THE DESIGN OF
URBAN SPACE

THE DESIGN OF URBAN SPACE

Richard M Cartwright

The Architectural Press Ltd: London
Halsted Press Division John Wiley & Sons, New York

First published 1980 in Great Britain by
The Architectural Press Ltd: London

© 1980 Department of Architecture and
Civic Design of the Greater London
Council.

Published in the USA by Halsted Press,
a Division of John Wiley & Sons, Inc.,
New York

British Library Cataloguing in Publication
Data

Greater London Council. *Department of
Architecture and Civic Design.*
    The design of urban space.
    1. Landscape architecture
    2. Streets — Accessories
    I. Title
    620'.417'32   SF472.7   80-
    41345

ISBN O-85139-693-3 (British edition)
ISBN 0-85139-694-1 Pbk
ISBN 0-470-27066-7 (United States
edition)

Filmset and printed in Great Britain
by BAS Printers Limited, Over Wallop,
Hampshire

Contents

Foreword

by Professor Sir Colin Buchanan, CBE, BSc, MRTPI, MICE, FRIBA

In broad terms cities may be said to consist of buildings and intervening spaces. The latter have traditionally served three functions: to accomodate the means of access to the buildings, to allow light, sunshine and air to penetrate, and to provide places where people can congregate for various social purposes. It has been a sad characteristic of city development over the last sixty years or so that the means of access function has, with the growth of motor traffic and all its unpleasant consequences, not only fouled the air but has seriously eroded the capability of the spaces to act as places where people can congregate. But all is not lost. At least the damage has been recognised, and the potential of the spaces for the betterment of city life is now clearly understood and is written into, implicity at any rate, the policies of most urban authorities. The difficulty of course, and it is a severe one, is to deal with the traffic, but even here progress is being made, and many towns can now boast of shopping streets and squares from which the worst of the traffic has been excluded.

At all events there is now good reason to take the design of urban spaces for public enjoyment more seriously than has perhaps been the case over the past few decades. Of course not everyone is enamoured of the street scenes which are appearing in our towns and cities. It has been said, wisely in my view, that recent architectural design has been more understandable and acceptable to the general public when it has been concerned more with the insides of buildings than with the outsides. People do seem to appreciate modern interior design with all its effects of lighting, colours, variations of levels, use of glass, contrasts of hard and soft furnishings and the display of pictures and sculptures; but when it comes to the outsides of buildings then many people seem puzzled and confused, with recurring complaints that the buildings are hard, harsh, smooth, angular, non-weathering and often overpowering in size.

Be that last point as it may, the manifest pleasure which is shown over interior or room design could, I believe, find equal expression in well-designed urban spaces which, after all, are, or could be, in a very real sense, the open rooms of the city. This is why I commend this publication from the Greater London Council. The book concentrates in a very practical way on the design of spaces. Reflecting, as it does, the experience of one of the largest urban authorities in the world, it should prove invaluable to all who are concerned with or interested in urban life and design. Perhaps I may be permitted to add one word of advice from my own experience. It is often said that good design costs no more than bad. I have found this to be only partially true. I have seen many a good design for an urban space absolutely ruined in the execution by the use of inferior materials and poor workmanship, broken paving slabs spotted with bitumen epitomise the matter. Quality counts, it may cost more in the beginning but it always pays in the end.

February 1980

Introduction

This book is intended to be used as a day to day design guide by those concerned with the design and upkeep of areas and spaces between buildings.

It is intended to alleviate repetitive research and to make more time available for creative thought and design.

The urban environment has become hard, over straight, complicated, dominant and hostile, not by any 'grand design' but by many small neglects.

It is up to everyone, from the planner and designer to the contractor and maintenance labourer, to try to form oases where human beings might wish to stay and belong.

For a successful environmental design there are seven major rules to follow:

Evaluate the human needs.
Keep designs simple.
Use organic forms, avoid straight lines.
Relate to human scale.
Avoid unnecessary expense.
Use natural materials where possible.
Avoid maintenance costs.

Dimensions

Throughout this book, all the dimensions given are metric and in mm, unless denoted otherwise. Where useful, overall sizes are provided together with component sizes where relevant. This should enable sketch schemes to be designed in sufficient detail for budget estimates to be prepared.

Consultations

Once a sketch scheme has been completed, the environmental designer should consult specialists as necessary in order to prepare the detail drawings.

Before any detail drawings are carried out, it is essential that the people who are to use the area, and the people who are responsible for the maintenance of that area, are consulted.

Tables of comparative costs

The tables list the alternatives in increasing order (cheapest first) of initial capital costs and are based on the costs of labour and materials, current on a level site in the London area at publication date, in accordance with a normal specification for the work involved. They include the cost of a foundation or substrate where required. The tables do not indicate actual rates for the work because:

These will vary with any change of specification.

They will also vary with location, soil conditions, tendering market conditions and other factors, but most of all, with inflation.

Nevertheless, the tables as published should generally be applicable for a number of years, provided that a normal specification is adhered to.

Some alternatives have been noted as being 'expensive' or 'very expensive'. These subjective comments are intended to help identify the alternatives which are in a different order of cost from the cheaper solutions.

It is false economy to save initial capital costs at the expense of subsequently high maintenance costs.

Useful names and addresses

The names and addresses of companies shown in this manual, are those of companies who produce goods and services which have been used by the Greater London Council.

Inclusion in this manual does not imply that such goods or services are currently approved by the GLC. The current approved lists must be checked.

It is hoped that this manual will be a good companion to the environmental designer. Any hints or suggestions arising from the use of this book are welcomed by the author.

Richard M Cartwright

SURFACING

Surfacing

The primary reason for putting a hard surface anywhere is to stop the load it carries – people, vehicles etc – from sinking into the ground, particularly in bad weather. It is normally multi-layered.

There are many secondary functions: water drainage, demarcation of zones, traffic management, introduction of colour and pattern etc which can be combined to create interest and scale.

Large flat expanses of hard surfacing should be avoided at any cost, except in kick-about sports areas or similar, and the main questions one should ask when considering the use of any hard surface materials are:

Is it absolutely necessary?

Must it be flat (though laid to falls of course)?

Would grass do instead?

What is the least percentage of hard to soft surfaces one can use to fulfil the primary function?

Only after these questions have been answered should the design stage begin.

1.1 In-situ paving

Definitions and uses

In situ flexible/concrete paving has previously been known as flexible/rigid paving. Flexible paving consists of compacted stone beneath a bituminous surface and concrete paving consists of a concrete slab laid either directly on the soil or on a granular bed. The concrete is sometimes covered by bituminous surfacing.

The paving is laid in situ, usually by machinery. The surface and foundations bear direct relationship to the load to be carried.

In this manual guides are given for surfacing materials and general foundations, but for detailed applications the relevant specialists must be consulted.

Materials and finishes

The most traditional surfacing materials are asphalt, tarmacadam (tar is in short supply and difficult to obtain), bitumen macadam and concrete. For anti-skid areas, epoxy-bitumen binder with coloured aggregate is laid on top of the existing surface.

Where hard bitumen binders are used the mixed material is called asphalt and where a softer binder is used, either of bitumen or tar, the material is called macadam. 'Bituminous bound' includes both bitumen and tar binders.

Relatively new materials which might be considered are artificial turf and synthetic rubber surfaces. There are also semi-rigid materials which combine the flexible characteristics of bitumen macadam with the hard wearing properties of cement concrete.

Bituminous based materials, colloquially called 'Black top' are, as Henry Ford would have said, 'Any colour so long as it's black' but coloured aggregate can be added which is generally 35%–40% of the mix. The aggregate colours range from greys to reds and greens. If more colour is required a clear binder with pigments is used, though at increased cost.

Anti-skid material colours are black, grey, red and green. Cement pigments; red, buff, yellow, green, blue, brown, black, grey, can be added to concrete mix. The resultant colours are fairly muted and with age tend to grey but nevertheless can be used to good effect.

Semi-rigid surfaces have the same colour range as cement pigments.

Artificial turf is generally green and the synthetic rubbers are brown or black.

The surface finish of vehicular paving,

where safety plays a major part, must be specified in collaboration with the relevant specialist engineers.

Where only light traffic is likely to occur, loose materials such as pea-shingle, gravel, hoggin, shale, cobbles and chippings may be used provided that the edges are retained (see 6.4 Edgings), the foundations are adequate (see 4.2 and 5.1), and that suitable supervision and security is available to prevent the loose material from being used as missiles.

Construction
For details see 4.2 Roads and 5.1 Footpaths.

Siting
For details see 4.3 Roads and 5.2 Footpaths.

Maintenance
Paving progressively deteriorates from the day it is opened to traffic. Flexible paving suffers mainly from deformation and pot-holing, and concrete paving suffers mainly from cracking. Maintenance costs are inversely proportional to first costs, therefore the better the construction of the paving the less maintenance will be needed throughout the designed life of the road, generally 40 years minimum.

The repair of flexible paving is easier, and less disruptive to traffic, than the repair of concrete paving.

If the paving is coloured it is not an unknown occurrence for statutory undertakers etc, to reinstate parts of the surface using 'Black top' with the resultant patchwork effect. Although this is only a temporary expedient, until the highway authority is able to permanently reinstate any surface imperfections, this state can sometimes persist for some considerable time. New coloured material is often different in colour, compared to the original weathered surface. The full agreement of the maintaining authority must be obtained before a coloured surface is specified.

It is better to specify unit paving (see 1.2) if colour is important.

If loose materials are used, they may frequently have to be collected, raked back into position and levelled or rolled.

Comparative costs
First dimension denotes thickness

100mm	Hoggin
100mm	Gravel
100mm	Loose chippings
100mm	Shale
150mm	Turf and top soil
100mm	Concrete Footpath
64mm	Black Tarmac footpath
64mm	Red Tarmac footpath
100mm	50mm dia loose flint cobbles
76mm	Black Tarmac road
76mm	Red Tarmac road
150mm	Reinforced concrete road
	Synthetic rubber/plastics – very expensive
	Artificial turf – very expensive

Recommendations
The choice of finishes for an area of in-situ paving is governed largely by the primary function of that area.

If colour is required for heavily used roads, unit paving (see 1.2) should be considered.

Large flat expanses of paving unless essential for ball games etc should be avoided, being both boring and costly.

When siting footpaths, remember that pedestrians tend to walk in straight lines between points of interest and will cut corners if it is at all possible.

Useful names (for addresses see chapter 21)
Amalgamated Roadstone Ltd
Brooklyns Westbrick Ltd
En-Tout-Cas Ltd
E J Elgood Ltd
Monsanto Ltd
Maxwell M Hart Ltd
Ronacrete Ltd
Rub-Kor UK Ltd
3M UK Ltd
Thomas Ness Ltd
Tarmac Roadstone Holdings Ltd
Watco (Sales) Ltd

1.2 Unit paving/ non-slip paving

Definitions and uses

Unit paving is defined as pre-cast factory produced units which when laid en masse on suitable foundations form a hard surface which is generally impervious. These vary in size from a standard brick pavior to a paving slab.

Materials and finishes

The most widely available materials are pre-cast concrete and brick.

Granite setts and cobbles are available both new and second hand and if money is no object natural stone and slate flags, terrazzo tiles and marble slabs may be considered.

Rubber tiles and rubber covered concrete slabs can be used for pedestrian traffic where noise and safety are of primary importance, for example childrens play areas.

Concrete is available as slabs and rectilinear or interlocking blocks in a wide range of pigmented colours and exposed aggregates. The texture of the surface varies from plain mould, through the exposed aggregates to moulded surfaces which can imitate setts, cobbles, York stone etc, or provide an anti-slip finish.

Brick and brick tile paviors are available in a wide range of colours and finishes. Since the inception of smoke abatement legislation true blues and blacks are no longer produced but a very large colour choice still exists; white, grey, yellow, buff, brown, red, blue-grey, purple and multi-coloured to name but few. The surface may be natural or glazed. It is essential that brick specified for paving is non-absorbent and frost resistant.

Granite setts and cobbles can be found in large quantities in most urban environments, being used almost universally throughout the 19th century, but the majority are now hidden under bituminous surfacing. Granite is very hard wearing and can be used either as a paving surface or as a deterrent surface: see 1.6 cobble hazard.

Granite colours range from greys and blues to greens and reds. Large areas of greys should be avoided unless there is a very pronounced paving pattern: see footpaths 5.3.

Granite and slate slabs are approximately 25-30mm thick and random rectangular in size. Slate colours are grey, dark-blue and green.

York stone and Portland stone slabs are 50mm thick and random rectangular in size. Colours are off-white, buff and yellow-white.

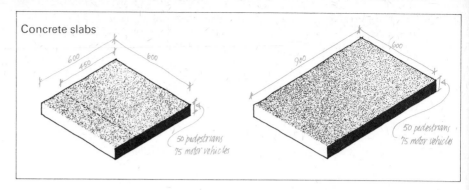

Concrete slabs

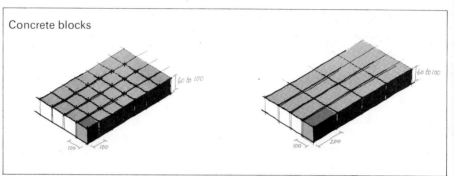

Concrete blocks

Marble slabs and Terrazzo tiles are approximately 20-40mm thick, with a variety of sizes and a wide range of colours; whites, pinks, greys, greens, reds etc. The surface is normally polished smooth.

Rubber and mat tiles 4–15mm thick and rubber covered concrete slabs 75mm thick have a variety of finishes; round studs, oblong studs, grained pattern etc.

The colours currently generally available are black, red, green, blue, brown and orange.

Construction and laying

For details see 4.2. Roads and 5.1. Footpaths.

Siting

For details see 4.3 Roads and 5.2 Footpaths.

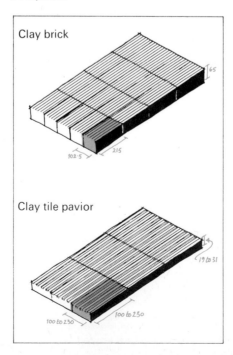

Clay brick

Clay tile pavior

Maintenance

Large maintenance costs are incurred when paving slabs adjacent to a road are broken by vehicles running/parking on them. In these situations small unit paving (blocks, bricks, setts) should be used.

In areas containing underground services which require occasional excavation, loose laid small unit paving should be used.

Damaged pre-cast concrete flags and bricks are generallly replaced with new units, but wherever possible natural stone should be repaired and re-used.

Comparative costs

First dimension denotes thickness

Pedestrian unit paving

50mm	Precast concrete paving slabs
65mm	Rough stock brick paving
65mm	Engineering brick paving – expensive
19mm	Quarry tiles – expensive
32mm	Quarry tiles – expensive
60mm	Interlocking block paving – expensive
65mm	Interlocking block paving – expensive
32mm	Terrazzo tiles – very expensive
50mm	York stone paving slabs – very
50mm	Portland stone – very expensive
32mm	Slate slabs – very expensive
32mm	Marble slabs – very expensive
25mm	Granite – very expensive

Vehicular unit paving

75mm	Vehicular precast concrete slabs
125mm	Precast concrete/grass firepath slabs
80mm	Interlocking block paving – expensive
100mm	Interlocking block paving – expensive

100mm	Second hand granite setts – very expensive
100mm	Granite Setts – very expensive

Recommendations
Use the least percentage of hard to soft surfaces possible to fulfil the primary function.

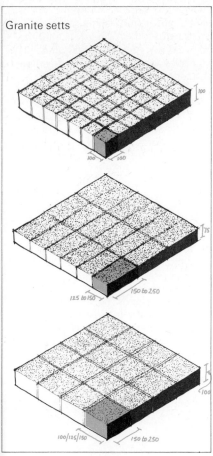

Granite setts

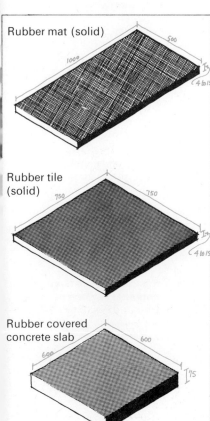

Rubber mat (solid)

Rubber tile (solid)

Rubber covered concrete slab

Small unit blocks/bricks/setts are preferable to slabs for general use. Where vehicles might over-run or park, small unit blocks can save maintenance costs.

Use units having colours sympathetic to earth and vegetation tones; browns, buffs, reds, yellows, greens and warm greys.

Colours should be selected to complement their immediate surroundings.

Avoid light colours which reflect glare from the sun.

Black, white and neutral greys generally tend to make areas dull and uninteresting, especially when wet.

Always try to obtain natural materials second hand, in the first instance.

Granite setts stripped of their bituminous overcoat can prove to be an effective speed deterrent and are also relatively maintenance free.

Where statutory services run under hard surfaces small unit paving should be specified. It is the easiest material to lift and replace and, of course, saves the cost of providing another surface material which all too often does not match the surrounding surfacing.

For small unit laying patterns see 5.3.

Useful names (for addresses see chapter 21)
ARC Concrete Ltd
Atlas Stone Co Ltd
Brick Advisory Centre
The Brick Development Association
British Dredging (Concrete Products) Ltd
Brooklyns Westbrick Ltd
Butterley Building Materials Ltd
Cement and Concrete Association
Charcon Products Ltd
Concrete (NI) Ltd
Eternit Building Products Ltd
Gerflex Ltd
Hawkins Tiles (Cannock) Ltd
Ibstock Brick Aldridge Ltd
Iudex Ltd
Marley Buildings Ltd
S Marshall & Sons Ltd
Mono Concrete Ltd
Natural Stone Directory
Noelite Ltd
Ockley Brick Co Ltd
Pirelli Ltd
Recticel Ltd
Redland Precast Ltd
Redland Tiles Ltd
Sevenoaks Brickworks Ltd
Charles Wicksteed & Co Ltd
Wooliscroft & Son Ltd

1.3 Tree pits/ surrounds/ grids

Definitions and uses
In the often hostile urban environment, trees have to be planted in specially prepared holes filled with top-soil. This pit can be a plain excavation or constructed so as to restrain the tree roots from spreading into nearby services or foundations, though at much increased cost over a plain excavated pit.

Tree surrounds/grids are the surface finish surrounding the tree trunk which allows surface water and air to penetrate the soil around the tree. The surround/grid must also allow for the natural expansion of the tree trunk.

Materials and finishes
Tree pits, where they are not plain excavations, are constructed from pre-cast concrete blocks or engineering bricks laid honeycomb or stretcher bond.

Tree surrounds/grids are generally brick, cobbles, pebbles, granite setts, pre-cast concrete or cast iron, usually natural finish. The tree surround can also be left as soil.

Raised kerbs or edgings should never be used round a tree as they obstruct the drainage of surface water to the roots and act as unsightly litter bins.

For completely solid-walled tree pits, built in stretcher bond, soil content must not be less than 8.0 m³.

Siting
Before siting trees near to underground services consult the statuatory undertakers and obtain their relevant drawings, though do not expect these to be absolutely accurate or up to date.

Trees planted next to a road should not be closer than 750mm measured from the kerb edge to the centre of the trunk. As a rough guide a large tree should not be planted closer than 5m to any obstruction if it is to mature into a perfect specimen, for two or more large specimen trees allow 10m between each, but of course the choice of species influences the spacing.

It is very rare, however, for an area to be large enough to support the growth of large specimen trees; sites are invariably limited to existing pavements and small plots of land. Generally in such sites it is best to plant as many trees as is physically possible, allowing them to grow into one another as and if they mature. Initially there can be large losses due to drought, disease and vandalism: a good end result will require initial apparent over-planting.

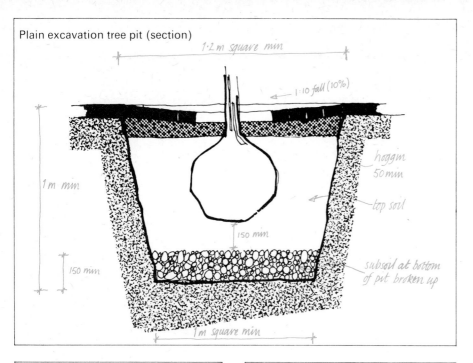

Plain excavation tree pit (section)

1·2 m square min

1:10 fall (10%)

hoggin 50 min

top soil

1m min

150 min

150 min

subsoil at bottom of pit broken up

1m square min

Small unit tree surround (plan)

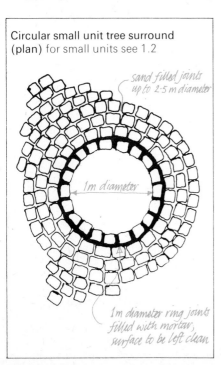

at least 15% must be permeable

joints filled with sand

centre line of units – joints filled with mortar. Surface of units to be left clean

Plain excavation tree pit with cast iron grid (section)

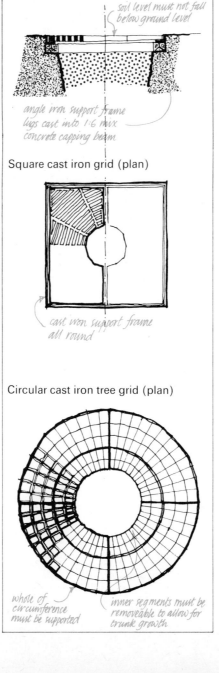

soil level must not fall below ground level

angle iron support frame lugs cast into 1:6 mix concrete capping beam

Square cast iron grid (plan)

cast iron support frame all round

Circular small unit tree surround (plan) for small units see 1.2

sand filled joints up to 2·5 m diameter

1m diameter

1m diameter ring joints filled with mortar, surface to be left clean

Circular cast iron tree grid (plan)

whole of circumference must be supported

inner segments must be removeable to allow for trunk growth

Maintenance

Properly constructed tree pits/surrounds require little maintenance apart from weeding, the topping up of settlement with top soil, and the removal of parts of the grid segments to allow for trunk growth. The level of the top-soil should not be allowed to fall below the tree grid: the void which results is virtually uncleanable and can harbour all manner of undesirable rubbish and weeds. Six visits are usually necessary during the first year, but two or three should suffice for each subsequent year for weeding and topping up.

Once the correct soil level round the trunk has been established it should not be raised or lowered. If it is necessary to raise the surrounding levels, cobbles or pebbles should be used to make up the difference, thus allowing air and water free access to the trunk and soil pocket. If it is necessary to lower the surrounding levels then at least 4m³ of soil for each tree should be contained within retaining walls with weep holes left at the new level to allow water to drain into the tree roots.

Concrete tree grids, and to some extent, cast-iron tree grids, need to be supported along the whole of their perimeter, with a reinforced concrete ring beam or galvanized steel angle frame, otherwise they are likely to fracture, even under the weight of pedestrians.

If a grid should protrude above the surrounding surface it will be a hazard for which the paving authority is liable.

Comparative costs

Single tree planted in pit including excavation, top-soil, stakes, guys and guards as necessary

3m standard tree
1m³ plain excavation

3m standard tree
1m³ block/brick walled pit

6m extra large nursery
4m³ plain excavation

6m extra large nursery
4m³ block/brick walled pit

10m semi-mature
8m³ plain excavation

10m semi-mature
8m³ block/brick walled pit

Additional costs for tree surrounds
First dimension denotes thickness

100mm	Top soil	
100mm	50mm dia loose flint cobbles – expensive	
65mm	Rough stock brick paving – expensive	
65mm	Engineering brick paving – expensive	
63mm	Precast concrete tree grille – expensive	
50mm	Red Staffordshire paviors – expensive	
100mm	Granite setts – very expensive	
25mm	Cast iron tree grille – very expensive	

Honeycomb built tree pit with cast iron grid (section)

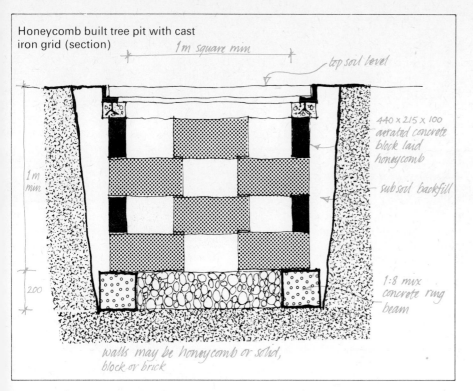

1m square min

top soil level

1m min

200

440 x 215 x 100 aerated concrete block laid honeycomb

sub soil backfill

1:8 mix concrete ring beam

walls may be honeycomb or solid, block or brick

Plan section through pit

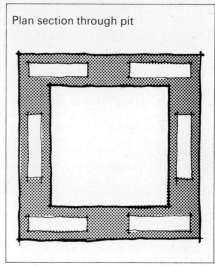

Tree pits near services

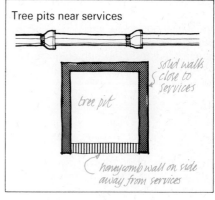

solid walls close to services

tree pit

honeycomb wall on side away from services

Trees planted next to roads

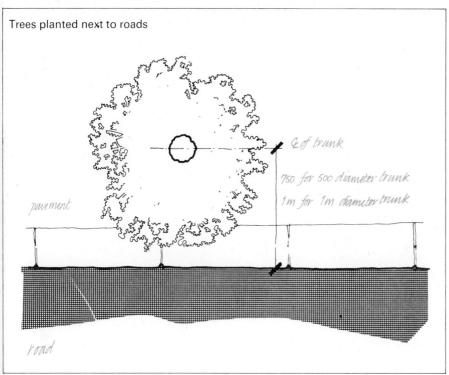

₵ of trunk

750 for 500 diameter trunk

1m for 1m diameter trunk

pavement

road

Changing paving levels around established trees

Raising level (section)

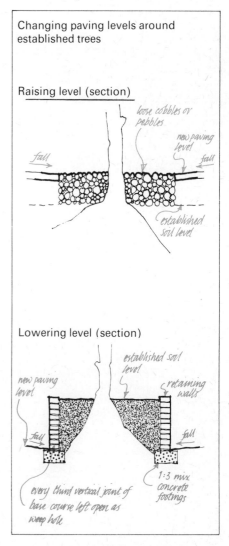

loose cobbles or pebbles

new paving level

fall

fall

established soil level

Lowering level (section)

established soil level

new paving level

retaining walls

fall

fall

1:3 mix concrete footings

every third vertical joint of base course left open as weep hole

Specimen tree spacing

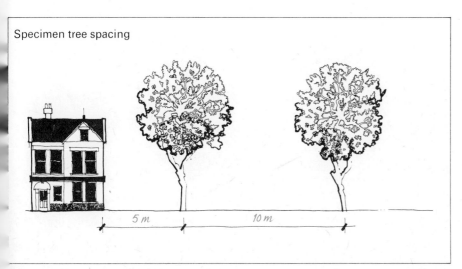

5 m

10 m

Recommendations

A tree pit should be large enough to support the initial growth of the tree it contains.

The surround must be at least 15% open soil, to allow air and moisture to penetrate to the tree roots.

If the surrounding paving is impervious it should be laid so that surface rainwater drains past tree pits 'en-route' to gulleys or channels.

For new standard trees planted in existing pavements a plain top soil surround is perfectly adequate and costs nothing. It is better value to put money towards extra trees than to specify expensive grids and surrounds: 3 standard trees = 1 standard tree + 1 cast iron grid.

When designing new areas of paving in which trees are to be planted, the trees can be used as the starting points from which paving layout patterns can be designed.

Effective formal areas can be designed by using circular or rectangular paving patterns radiating from tree grids.

Circular tree surrounds do not combine well with flagged areas, but work better with in situ finishes and small unit paving, which can radiate outwards as intersecting circles with the trees as the centres.

Where the site does not lend itself to formal design, random planting and paving can often provide a more interesting solution: see 5.3 Patterns.

During the first year of planting it is essential that the tree is frequently watered and that the top soil level is kept topped up and weed free.

Useful names (for addresses see chapter 21)
Atlas Stone Ltd
Brickhouse Dudley Ltd
Concrete (NI) Ltd
S Marshall and Sons Ltd
Mather and Smith Ltd
Mono Concrete Ltd
Pullen Foundries Ltd
Sloan and Davidson Ltd

1.4 Pavement lights/gratings/ cellar flaps

Definitions and uses

Pavement lights are glass blocks set into pavements in grids.

Pavement gratings are metal grilles set into pavements.

Cellar flaps or doors, generally hinged upwards to open, are set into pavements.

They are used to admit light, light and air, or access to basement workshops, storerooms, vaults, cellars etc, many of which still run under pavements and roads.

Pavement lights/gratings/flaps are usually found between the edges of pavements and buildings though occasionally they are positioned in the middle of pavements.

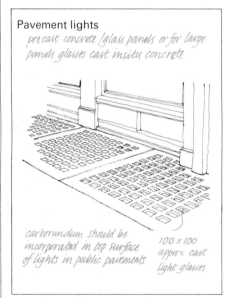

Pavement lights

pre cast concrete/glass panels or for large panels glasses cast insitu concrete

carborundum should be incorporated in top surface of lights in public pavements

100 x 100 approx cast light glasses

Pavement lights transmit light but not air. Where provision has to be made in pavements for smoke exits in case of fire, pavement lights are used which can be broken by the fire brigade but which support normal foot traffic. Smoke extract panels must be indicated by means of 100mm x 75mm minimum size metal or plastic plates fixed vertically nearby or cast into the surface of the panels. Counter balanced escape flaps, single leaf 600mm x 600mm opening, sometimes have to be provided in panels of pavement lights.

Gratings are psychologically disturbing to walk on and can be dangerous to small animals and to the wearers of thin high heels etc. They are pervious to rain, dirt, litter and other unmentionables and nowadays have been largely replaced by pavement lights, especially since the advent of good mechanical ventilation.

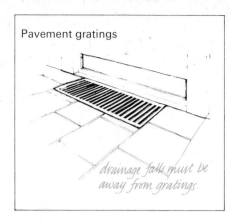

Pavement gratings

drainage falls must be away from gratings.

Cellar flaps provide access to cellars

Materials and finishes

Pavement lights are made from cast glass blocks which are normally cast into panels of either pre-cast or insitu concrete. In public footpaths, carborundum is incorporated into the top surface of the lights to provide an antislip surface.

Where the lights will be subject to loads from iron shod trolley wheels etc, each light is set in a metal collar which allows easy repair by normal maintenance workmen.

Gratings are normally made from cast iron or steel, painted black and set into concrete or a metal frame.

Cellar flaps are usually made from galvanised steel plate with a non-skid surface or from hardwoods which require no preservative treatment – iroko, teak etc. In the open position metal chains or rails should be used to prevent passers-by from falling into the opening. Metal flap doors can be very slippery and dangerous in icy or wet weather.

Cellar flaps

always secure guard rail or chain when the flaps are left open

Siting

The siting of pavement lights/gratings/ flaps bears direct relationship to what is happening underneath and as such will be relatively invariable for any particular location.

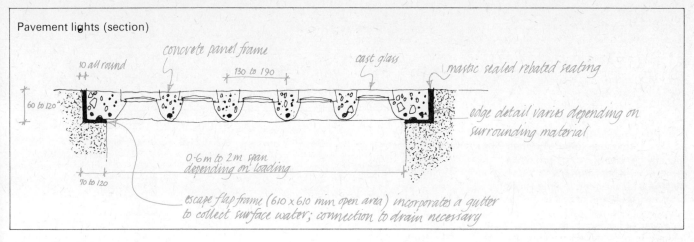

Pavement lights (section)

10 all round
concrete panel frame
130 to 190
cast glass
mastic sealed rebated seating
60 to 120
edge detail varies depending on surrounding material
70 to 120
0·6 m to 2 m span depending on loading
escape flap frame (610 × 610 min open area) incorporates a gutter to collect surface water; connection to drain necessary

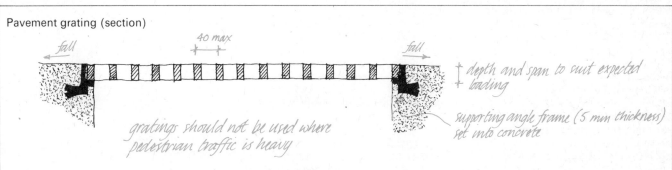

Pavement grating (section)

fall
40 max
fall
depth and span to suit expected loading
supporting angle frame (5 mm thickness) set into concrete
gratings should not be used where pedestrian traffic is heavy

Lights can be located almost anywhere.

Gratings should not be used where there is heavy foot traffic or small wheeled trolleys etc.

Flaps should not be so large, or ill-sited, that they completely obstruct any footpath when in the open position. In hot weather, cellar flaps are sometimes left open all day, with accompanying hazard and inconvenience to passers by.

Cellar flaps

section

guard bar

down pipe to drain

gutter frame set into concrete

plan

1·2 m normal

1·2 m normal

Special approval is required from the highway authority before any lights/gratings or flaps may be placed in public footpaths.

Maintenance
Lights are very tough and seldom require maintenance, but if very heavy traffic is expected, the lights should be of the metal collar type which can be replaced by normal maintenance personnel.

Gratings require little maintenance, apart from occasional painting and checking of anchorage points for corrosion. If the corrosion exceeds specified limits, the whole grille should be replaced.

Flaps are subject to wear, both from passing traffic and from the actions of opening and closing. Metal generally requires less maintenance than timber, but cannot be repaired so readily. Hinges and fasteners require occasional cleaning and oiling.

Recommendations
Though initially more expensive, pavement lights are preferable to grilles.

Care should be taken to select the correct edging section for the lights, as this is influenced by the surrounding materials.

Make sure that general falls are maintained over lights and flaps and away from grilles.

In public footpaths timber cellar flaps are preferred because of the danger of slipping associated with metal cellar flaps.

Useful names (for addresses see chapter 21)
Healey John (London) Ltd
J A King (Glascrete) Ltd
Luminor Ltd
Luxcrete Ltd

1.5 Manhole/ inspection covers

Definitions and uses

Covers of one sort or another often have to be inserted into surface finishes. They usually consist of a cast-iron cover fitting into a cast-iron frame, sometimes having a clear opening wide enough to admit the passage of a man. The covers can either hinge to open, or be removed completely for access to gas taps, coal cellars, water valves, fire hydrants, telephone junction boxes, electrical services, drains, sewers and so on.

The clear openings vary in size from 150mm x 150mm to 1.2m x 0.75m. The minimum size necessary to admit a man is 600mm square or diameter.

Covers should be non-rocking, sliding or tilting in use; thus a square opening generally has two separate triangular covers each bearing on three points. The covers have holes cast in the top surface into which lifting keys locate to open them, though it is not unknown for a labourer's strategically placed pick-end to fulfil the same purpose. All covers should have an anti-skid surface.

Materials and finishes

Heavy and medium duty covers and frames are usually made from cast-iron. Light duty covers and frames or boxes can be made from cast-iron, aluminium, pre-cast concrete, or more recently glass reinforced concrete, all left in their natural finish.

Light and medium duty covers can be recessed to incorporate material to match the surrounding finish.

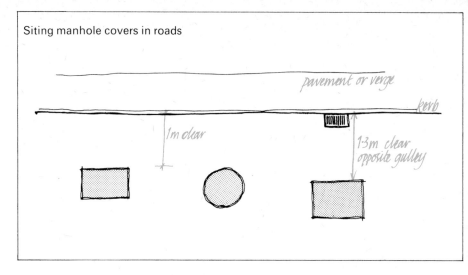

Siting manhole covers in roads

pavement or verge

kerb

1m clear

1.3m clear opposite gulley

The most hazardous locations are on bends in roads and in the middle of footpaths, but if these sites cannot be avoided the greatest care must be taken to ensure that the frame and cover are perfectly flush with the surrounding surface and true to falls.

Even perfectly installed covers in roads are a hazard to cyclists, particularly when wet. A minimum distance of 1.0m should be left clear between any cover and the kerb and opposite a gully this distance should be increased to 1.3m.

In footpaths the problem of differential settlement between cover frames and the footpath material can be diminished by inserting small unit-paving between the cover frame and the footpath to form a semi-flexible frame.

Maintenance

Apart from cleaning dirt from the bearing points and hinges, covers require no maintenance. In the rare event of a cover being broken it should be replaced before any traffic is allowed to run over it.

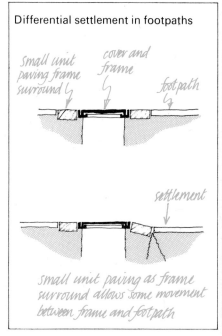

Differential settlement in footpaths

small unit paving frame surround

cover and frame

footpath

settlement

small unit paving as frame surround allows some movement between frame and footpath

expected loads, if in doubt assume the worst.

As covers/frames are, in the main, obligatory, little can be achieved environmentally with them except for careful siting and frame surround detailing.

In roads, leave at least 1.0m clear between covers and kerb.

Avoid siting covers on sharp bends in roads carrying fast moving traffic.

Covers/frames must be set perfectly flush with the surrounding surfacing.

If road and footpath levels are altered, due to resurfacing etc, the covers/frames must be reset to the new levels.

Useful names (for addresses see chapter 21)
Brickhouse Dudley Ltd
Broads Manufacturing Co Ltd
Mono Concrete Ltd
John Needham & Sons Ltd
Stanton & Staveley Ltd
A C Woodrow & Co Ltd

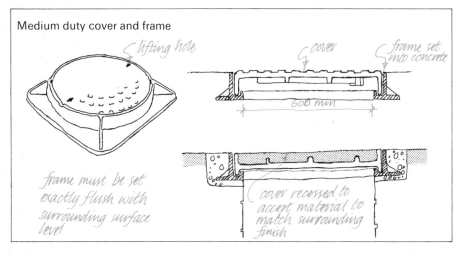

Medium duty cover and frame

lifting hole

cover

frame set into concrete

600 min

frame must be set exactly flush with surrounding surface level

cover recessed to accept material to match surrounding finish

Siting

Manhole/Inspection covers have to be sited above the services to which they relate, but nevertheless they can often be located along the line of the service so that they provide the minimum inconvenience when in use and the minimum danger when closed.

A cover should never be left in the open position unless it is surrounded by barriers, or a person is in attendance to divert road or foot traffic round it.

Recommendations

Always ensure that the covers/frames are strong enough to withstand the

1.6 Deterrent paving

Definitions and uses
Deterrent Paving/Surfacing is defined as material which can be used to discourage the passage of pedestrians and/or vehicles.

Surfaces which deter pedestrians will not necessarily deter vehicles though surfaces which deter vehicles usually do deter pedestrians.

Materials and finishes
Any paving material which can be laid as a deterrent, for example deep loose sand, gravel, pebbles, cobbles etc may be used, but beside the problems associated with loose materials (see 1.1), it is generally easier to use either pre-cast concrete paving slabs having small (pedestrian) or large (vehicle) pyramid shaped projections. Alternatively cobbles cast in concrete, either in situ or as pre-cast slabs, may be used.

Pre-cast concrete slabs, with or without cobbles, are by their very nature uninviting and aggressive, and do little to improve the environment.

Shrubs, bushes and trees are equally effective as a deterrent, and infinitely preferable on environmental grounds. Heather, hawthorn, brambles and gorse are not to be jumped into lightly, and are soon treated with respect by the unwary.

Hard mounds also make good pedestrian and vehicle deterrents.

Siting
Deterrent paving/surfacing should be sited in areas where it is undesirable or dangerous for pedestrians and/or vehicles to go. For example: traffic islands near fast moving traffic, areas where vehicles should not park; areas close to buildings in housing estates, underneath head-height projections from buildings (ergonomically undesirable but unfortunately all too prevalent) and so on.

Only where it is absolutely impossible to use either shrubs, bushes, trees or hard mounds, should loose materials or concrete deterrent paving be used.

Maintenance
Any material which prevents access by foot or vehicle is, of course, uncleanable and difficult to maintain. The best materials to use are those which are self-cleansing, or hide litter and dirt, and are also virtually maintenance free.

Shrubs, bushes, trees and hard surface mounds require less maintenance than pre-cast concrete deterrent slabs and loose materials.

Comparative costs
First dimension denotes thickness

100mm	Loose sand
100mm	Loose gravel
100mm	Loose pebbles
100mm	50mm dia loose flint cobbles
75mm	Deterrent flags (pedestrian) – expensive
75mm	Deterrent flags (vehicular) – expensive
75mm	Cobble stone flags – very expensive
100mm	In situ cobble paving – very exensive

Shrubs, bushes and trees – vary in cost depending on type, size and spacing. Hard mound costs vary with details.

Recommendations
Deterrent paving slabs/surfacing should only be used as a last resort.

If it is not possible to design deterrent areas out of a scheme then, shrubs, bushes, trees or hard mounds should be considered first.

Loose materials are cheaper and easier

Precast concrete deterrent paving slabs

pedestrian

40-50 mm flint cobbles
85 Kg weight
65
600 or 900
600

44 Kg weight
75
600
600

vehicular
180
600
300
36 Kg weight

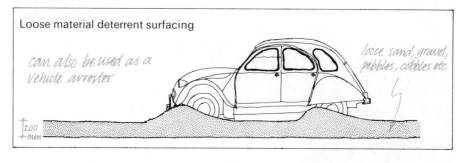

Loose material deterrent surfacing

can also be used as a vehicle arrester

loose sand, gravel, pebbles, cobbles etc

200 mm

Shrubs, bushes and trees as a deterrent

Only select hardy species which can tolerate road splash and pollution

plant right up to kerb

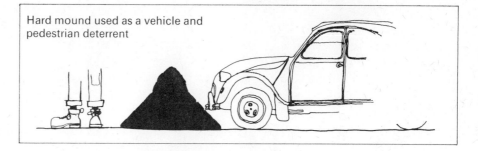

Hard mound used as a vehicle and pedestrian deterrent

to lay than pre-cast slabs, but require some security to deter unauthorized use or abuse; such as their removal for missiles.

It must be immediately apparent from a distance that an area is 'no go'; it is very dangerous for a person to be trapped between vehicles and deterrent areas.

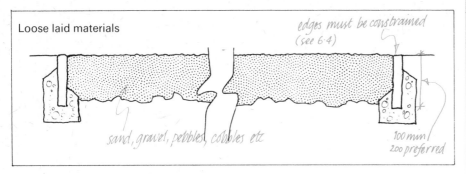

Loose laid materials

edges must be constrained (see 6·4)

sand, gravel, pebbles, cobbles etc

100 mm 200 preferred

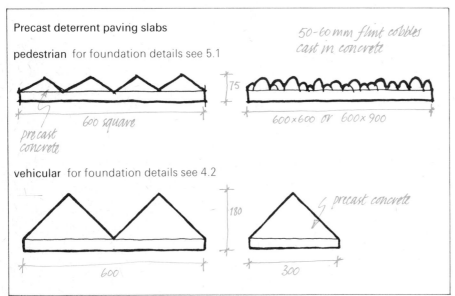

Precast deterrent paving slabs

pedestrian for foundation details see 5.1

50-60 mm flint cobbles cast in concrete

75

600 square

precast concrete

600×600 or 600×900

vehicular for foundation details see 4.2

180

precast concrete

600

300

Shrubs, bushes and trees used as a deterrent

plants must be particularly hardy and resistant to road splash etc; for sizes and planting details see 2·1

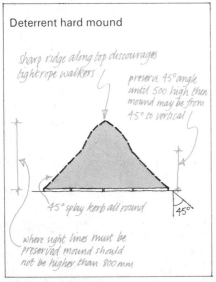

Deterrent hard mound

sharp ridge along top discourages tightrope walkers

preserve 45° angle until 500 high then mound may be from 45° to vertical

45° splay kerb all round

45°

where sight lines must be preserved mound should not be higher than 800 mm

Useful names (for addresses see chapter 21)
S Marshall & Sons Ltd
Mono Concrete Ltd
Townscape Products Ltd

1.7 Mounds and slopes

Definitions and uses

Artificial mounds and slopes make a very valuable contribution to the environment. They can be so large as virtually to become mountains or so small as to be little bigger than molehills.

Mounds slope down in all directions from the summit generally to a common level, whereas slopes tend to be unidirectional from one level to another.

Mounds can be used for sound and sight barriers (see 4.1) and, if large enough, recreational pursuits.

Slopes are used to change levels, particularly where it is desirable to use wheelchairs, prams or trolleys and slopes also can have positive recreational benefits, whether they are hard-surfaced or grassy.

mound   slope

Mounds and slopes are far more interesting visually than flat areas of grass and paving, and in difficult ground conditions are a good way of providing enough top soil to support the growth of trees and plants.

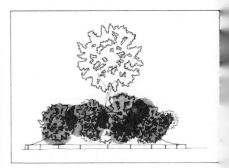

Materials and finishes

Materials each have their own maximum angle of slope which they assume when they are heaped up (response) or cut (repose), this slope cannot be exceeded without reinforcement of some kind; plant and tree roots, plastic or wire mesh staked in place, longitudinal boards and frames, retaining walls etc: see 7.4

Mounds and slopes are generally made from hardcore or gravel and sand, and covered with hard impervious surfacing material, or top soil which is planted with shrubs and trees or grassed over.

Virtually any hard finish suitable for footpaths can be used as a surface (see 1.1 and 1.2) In situ concrete can be impossible to hold in place on steep slopes, so be warned!

If top soil is used it should have a minimum depth of 150mm and be stabilised against erosion especially if the vegetation has not yet become fully grown.

Construction and fixing
Slopes expressed as gradients, percentages, and angles from the horizontal.

1 in 0.2	= 500%	= 78.7° or 78°42'
1 in 0.4	= 250%	= 68.2° or 68°12'
1 in 0.6	= 166%	= 59.0° or 59°
1 in 0.8	= 125%	= 51.3° or 51°18'
1 in 1	= 100%	= 45.0° or 45°
1 in 2	= 50%	= 26.6° or 26°36'
1 in 4	= 25%	= 14.0° or 14°
1 in 6	= 16.6%	= 9.5° or 9°30'
1 in 8	= 12.5%	= 7.1° or 7°6'
1 in 10	= 10%	= 5.7° or 5°42'
1 in 12	= 8.3%	= 4.7° or 4°42'
1 in 20	= 5%	= 2.9° or 2°54'
1 in 40	= 2.5%	= 1.4° or 1°24'
1 in 60	= 1.6%	= 0.95° or 0°57'
1 in 80	= 1.25%	= 0.72° or 0°43'
1 in 100	= 1%	= 0.57° or 0°34'
1 in 200	= 0.5%	= 0.29° or 0°17'
1 in 400	= 0.25%	= 0.14° or 0°8'
1 in 600	= 0.16%	= 0.10° or 0°6'
1 in 800	= 0.125%	= 0.07° or 0°4'
1 in 1000	= 0.1%	= 0.05° or 0°3'
1 in 5000	= 0.02%	= 0.01° or 0°0.6'

Siting
For siting and size of mounds to act as sight and sound barriers see 4.1

Mounds and slopes should be sited where they can make the maximum environmental contribution, for example to break up visually large flat areas, and to reduce the scale of large buildings and objects. A mound as small as 1m high and 3–4m across can have a considerable impact on a large space.

Deterrent mounds and slopes should not be closer than 0.5m to a road.

Mounds and slopes should not be closer than –
   0.5m to a road carrying light traffic
   1m to a boundary or building
   3m to a road carrying heavy traffic.

Maintenance
Hard mounds and slopes are self cleansing and draining, and maintenance should be low.

Soft mounds and slopes can vary between negligible maintenance for hardy vegetation and trees, to high maintenance for ornamental grass. If a motor mower is required to cut the grass, access and off road parking should be provided for its transporter.

Comparative costs
The comparative costs of suitable small unit mound surfacing materials have roughly the same order as unit paving laid on the flat: see 1.2.

Precast concrete slabs, however, become considerably more expensive, due to the additional cost of cutting

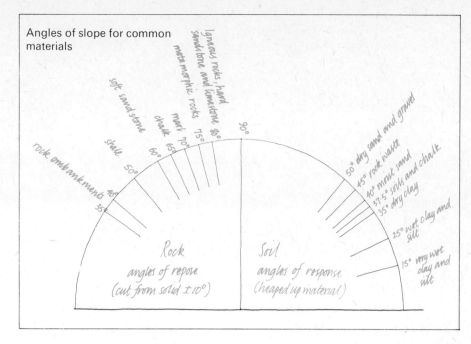

Angles of slope for common materials

Rock
angles of repose
(cut from solid ± 10°)

Soil
angles of response
(heaped up material)

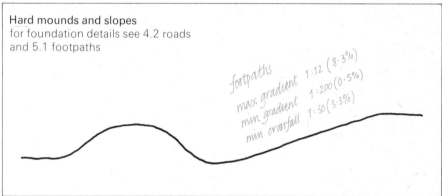

Hard mounds and slopes
for foundation details see 4.2 roads and 5.1 footpaths

footpaths
max. gradient 1:12 (8.3%)
min gradient 1:200 (0.5%)
min crossfall 1:30 (3.3%)

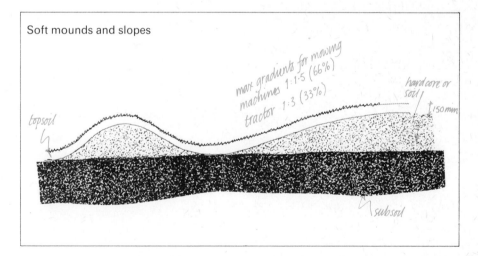

Soft mounds and slopes

max gradients for mowing machines 1:1.5 (66%)
tractor 1:3 (33%)

hard core or soil
150mm

topsoil

subsoil

which becomes inevitable when forming them into 800mm high mounds. It is not good practice to use slabs as mound surfacing unless the mounds are very large and have large radii of curvature (at least 2m).

Recommendations
Wherever possible, mounds and slopes should be introduced into the environment, especially if it is flat.

Although it is far more difficult to design in three dimensions and curves, rather than two dimensions and straight lines, the extra effort needed is more than offset by the immeasurable benefit to the environment.

Grass and shrub planted mounds and slopes are among the cheapest initially, but have a subsequent maintenance cost which may be low or high depending on species.

In areas with high rates of vandalism it may be very difficult to establish and maintain vegetation, but it is always worth the initial effort. In specifying for such mounds, the cost of replanting for one or two seasons should be allowed. Normally after this length of time the amount of vandalism subsides considerably. If this fails however, the mounds and slopes can always be surfaced later with in situ or unit paving.

Planting

In order to soften the predominantly hard urban environment, planting should be introduced wherever possible. Even the most hostile areas can become more hospitable and sympathetic to human beings, following the introduction of grass, shrubs, trees and so on.

In the open urban environment, plants generally have to endure far more severe conditions than those found either in nature or in domestic and private gardens. Nonetheless, an examination of established gardens in an area, will give some indication as to the type of planting likely to succeed nearby.

To be successful, plants need the appropriate type of soil, conditions and maintenance, and for the first two years, while becoming established, they also need to be guarded against vandalism and in any case funds should be set aside for the replacement of damaged plants during this period.

It is important that plants are chosen to match the structure and chemical characteristics of the soil in which they are to be planted. Generally, light sandy soil is free draining and acidic whilst heavy clay soil tends to be water retentive. The best type of soil is a neutral loam but this is rarely found in the urban environment.

Whilst, for example, bulky organic material can be added to light sandy or chalky soil to aid water and nutritional retention, and lime can be added to acid soils to make them more neutral, the composition of the soil can be altered only to a relatively small degree and it is important to select species of plants which are tolerant of the particular type of soil in an area.

Most plants need sunlight for successful growth, particularly the flowering varieties, but some species thrive well in shaded conditions and can be successfully used in built-up areas where sunlight is limited.

Where the prevailing wind, or the wind tunnel effect between tall buildings, is likely to present problems, a line or mass of hardy plants can be used to provide shelter for species less able to endure windy conditions, including homo sapiens.

If a site has extreme conditions of soil, climate and ground and air polution, expert advice should be obtained before plants are selected. For new planting in the urban environment the chances of failure can be lessened considerably by sensible design, good preparation, careful choice of plant species, and the establishment of a maintenance programme.

Before designing any planting scheme for an urban area it is vital to know what maintenance resources are available. As a rule, formal gardens require constant maintenance and at the other extreme natural areas, containing hardy and vigorous plants, require virtually no maintenance. In times when the cost of maintenance is rapidly increasing, it is often necessary to design areas which can be left largely to their own devices without detriment.

Maintenance must be regarded as an integral part of the design. Unsympathetic, wrongly directed maintenance can be as destructive as vandalism and result in the complete destruction of planting schemes.

Water is essential to all planting and so watering points must be provided near all planting areas (roughly every 50m).

2.1 Plant types

In order to prepare sketch designs, the environmental designer should be aware of the basic different types of planting, their sizes and their uses.

Grass
Turf is more expensive than seeded grass but becomes established much quicker.

Ground Cover
Ground cover is more expensive than grass but will require little or no maintenance, once established.

It is useful for areas having difficult access, raised traffic islands and so on.

Seeded grass
seeding best in August, September. Less good alternative April, May. Established in 8–12 months, sports areas 18–24 months

top soil
(150 mm on steep slopes)
subsoil

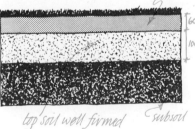

Turf grass
established in 3–6 months

turf
60
100
top soil well firmed
subsoil

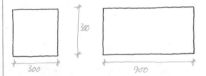

Standard turf sizes

300
300
900

Ground cover
once properly established it excludes weeds

ground cover planting
25–100
100 min
top soil (150 min on steep slopes) subsoil
must be weed free before planting

Shrubs
A shrub is a plant with woody stems branching from the root.

Shrubs can be bushy, arching, long stemmed, picturesque, columnar, have large or small leaves and flowers etc.

Shrubs
planting seasons: deciduous – November to March, conifers and evergreens – September to May 400 mm minimum top soil (600 mm on steep slopes)

low shrub
1·5 m to
2·5 m

medium shrubs
2·5 m to
4·5 m

tall shrubs
4·5 m plus

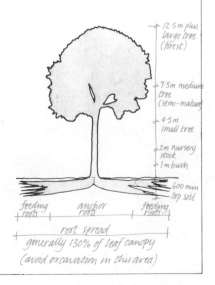

Trees
planting seasons: deciduous – October to March, conifers and evergreens – October to May 600 mm minimum top soil (900 mm on steep slopes) for tree pits see chapter 1.3

12·5 m plus large tree (forest)
7·5 m medium tree (semi-mature)
4·5 m small tree
2m nursery stock
1m bush
600 min top soil

feeding roots   anchor roots   feeding roots
root spread
generally 130% of leaf canopy
(avoid excavation in this area)

Simplified tree shapes
Trees can have light or heavy foliage. Light foliage allows light to penetrate through while heavy foliage provides shade from the sun.

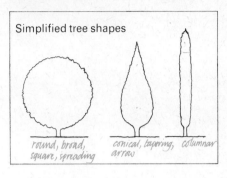

Simplified tree shapes

round, broad, square, spreading   conical, tapering, arrow   columnar

Tree planting (Typical pavement tree)
Trees are supplied from nurseries with bare roots, with roots grown in containers or (for large trees) roots contained in a soil ball.

Planting should not be carried out if the soil is wet or waterlogged, in a period of drought, or if frost is in the soil.

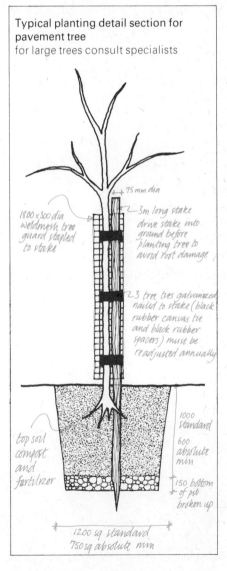

Typical planting detail section for pavement tree
for large trees consult specialists

75 mm dia
1800 x 300 dia weldmesh tree guard stapled to stake
3m long stake drive stake into ground before planting tree to avoid root damage
2.3 tree ties galvanized nailed to stake (black rubber canvas tie and black rubber spacers) must be readjusted annually
top soil compost and fertilizer
1000 standard
600 absolute min
150 bottom of pit broken up
1200 sq standard 750 sq absolute min

Screens and hedges
Trees and bushes planted close together will form light, sound and wind screens and may also filter out a certain amount of dust.

Screens and hedges

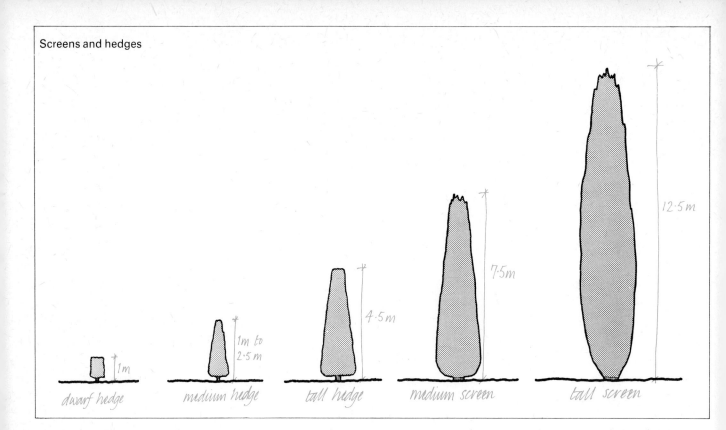

1m

dwarf hedge

1m to 2·5 m

medium hedge

4·5 m

tall hedge

7·5 m

medium screen

12·5 m

tall screen

WATER

Water

Open water is an invaluable asset, particularly in the largely man made urban environment.

It comes in a variety of forms; rain, fountains, puddles, ditches, streams, ponds, pools, canals, lakes, rivers, reservoirs and seas. Some of these are relatively easy to add into an environmental design scheme, others occur naturally and must be used as they are.

Open water is contained in either area or linear form. Generally, area water is relatively static and linear water mobile.

Although, within specified limits, water is an environmental asset, provision must be made to control any flooding with its attendant danger, discomfort and cost. Normally this can be done by draining away any excess and/or restricting the intake where possible. Where the water may storm down from 'on high' it is essential to build-in adequate drainage.

Open water has a multitude of uses:

Natural – visual and wildlife.
Drinking.
Transport.
Power Source.
Recreation.

Many of these uses can be combined in the same stretch of water, though activities which might cause pollution, such as power boating, are not allowed on drinking water supply reservoirs.

In the urban environment generally, drinking water has no relevance as open water. By the time it reaches towns and cities, it is usually hidden in pipes.

3.1 Drainage channels

Definitions and uses
Drainage channels are used wherever rain water needs to be drained away from hard surfaces; along footpaths, roads, runways, car parks, pedestrian areas and so on.

Materials and finishes
Surface water channels are usually made from granite setts, brick or pre-cast concrete, left in their natural finish. They can be dished or recessed.

Undersurface channels are made from either pre-cast concrete units having a circular bore fed from a continuous slot in the top surface or cast iron gratings over a concrete or cast iron channel, all finishes left natural.

Construction and fixing
Minimum falls:
crossfalls – 1 in 50 (2%)
surface channels – 1 in 200 (0.5%)
undersurface channels – 1 in 1000 (0.1%).

Siting
Channels are sited at the junctions of impervious surfaces and raised kerbs, and at junctions where impervious areas fall towards each other, particularly if they are dissimilar.

Channels between roads and kerbs are usually left as a chip-free area of asphalt adjacent to the kerb, or in mastic asphalt where falls are critical.

Channels sited between roads and pedestrian pavements can incorporate raised projections which cause a considerable noise to be made when they are run over by a vehicle tyre. This warns the driver that he is about to leave his apportioned space and should do something about it; it also encourages any passers by to leap away before it is too late.

Where there is heavy pedestrian traffic only types 4, 5, 6 and 7 should be used due to the dangers of tripping and twisted ankles associated with the others. Cast iron, type 6, is very expensive and is only used nowadays in areas of special historic interest.

Where the gradient is less than 1 in 200 (0.5%) type 7 should be used. This has the advantage of draining along its whole length, thus eliminating ponding between gullies and the need for artificial summits and valleys. Inspection covers should be provided at all stop ends and at roughly 30m intervals.

Maintenance
Surface channels require little

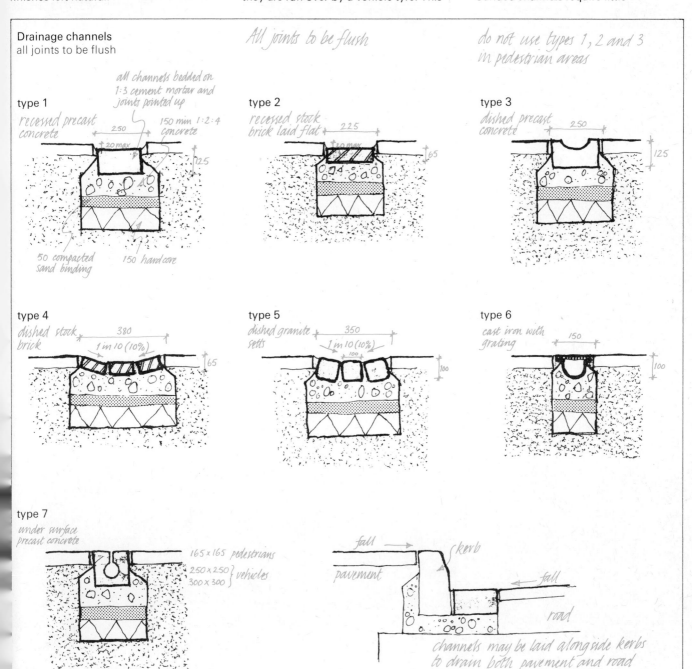

Drainage channels
all joints to be flush

All joints to be flush

do not use types 1, 2 and 3 in pedestrian areas

type 1
recessed precast concrete
all channels bedded on 1:3 cement mortar and joints pointed up
150 min 1:2:4 concrete
2.50
20 max
125
50 compacted sand binding
150 hardcore

type 2
recessed stock brick laid flat
2.25
10 max
65

type 3
dished precast concrete
2.50
125

type 4
dished stock brick
380
1 in 10 (10%)
65

type 5
dished granite setts
350
1 in 10 (10%)
100

type 6
cast iron with grating
150
100

type 7
under surface precast concrete
165 x 165 pedestrians
250 x 250 } vehicles
300 x 300 }

fall   *kerb*
pavement   *fall*
road
channels may be laid alongside kerbs to drain both pavement and road

21

maintenance other than regular brushing to remove dirt and sediment.

Undersurface channels require the surface slot or grille to be kept clean by surface brushing, and occasional water flushing by a gully cleaning machine on a normal tour of operation. Where, due to neglect, low pressure water flushing is not effective, dry rodding or high pressure water jetting may be needed.

Comparative costs
Type 1 Standard precast concrete, flat.
Type 3 Precast concrete, dished.
Type 2 Stock brick, recessed.
Type 7 Precast concrete, under surface
        – expensive.
Type 4 Stock brick, dished –
        expensive.
Type 5 Granite setts, dished –
        expensive.
Type 6 Cast iron grating – very
        expensive.

Recommendations
Where the channel is laid next to a kerb it preferably should be identical, in material, colour and finish, to the kerb, otherwise uneven striping occurs.

In areas carrying heavy pedestrian traffic the order of preference is:-
Type 7 Precast concrete, undersurface.
Type 4 Brick, dished.
Type 5 Stone setts, dished.
Type 6 Cast iron grating and channel
        only to be used in historic
        areas.
Types 1, 2 and 3 must not be used.

Bituminous materials and concrete can be laid such that the drainage channel is part of the parent material and does not necessitate the introduction of a special and separate element.

To avoid ponding, undersurface draining should be used when the gradients are less than 1 in 200 (0.5%).

Useful names (for addresses see chapter 21)
Atlas Stone Co Ltd
Broads Manufacturing Co Ltd
Charcon Products Ltd
Concrete (Northern Ireland) Ltd

3.2 Gulleys

Definitions and uses
A gully is the hole in the ground into which surface water drains, as a trickle or a torrent, to the main drainage system and ultimately to the sea.

In order to prevent objects, like feet and wheels, from disappearing down the gully, a grating, made of cast iron or steel, is usually used to cover the hole.

Gratings are available as:
light duty for pedestrian traffic
medium duty for a wheel load up to 5 tonnes
heavy duty for a wheel load up to 11.5 tonnes.

Kerb type gully covers and frames are available to match vertical, 45° splay and 12°–15° half battered kerbs, and have the advantage of not projecting into the road to be tripped over or skidded on as is sometimes the case with horizontal gratings.

Materials and finishes
Light duty gully gratings can be made from cast iron, aluminium, steel or pre-cast concrete.

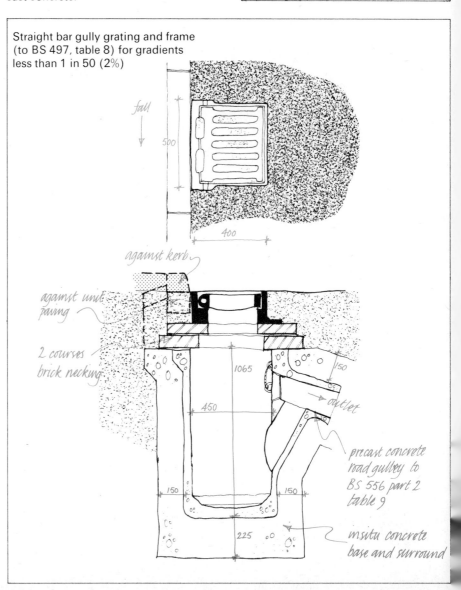

Storm bar gully grating and frame (as BS 497, table 8) for gradients steeper than 1 in 50 (2%)—left hand shown

fall
500
400

Straight bar gully grating and frame (to BS 497, table 8) for gradients less than 1 in 50 (2%)

fall
500
400

against kerb
against unit paving
2 courses brick necking
1065
150
450
outlet
precast concrete road gulley to BS 556 part 2 table 9
insitu concrete base and surround
150
150
225

Medium and heavy duty gully gratings are usually made from cast iron, steel or pre-cast concrete.

Usually gully gratings are left in their natural finish.

Construction and fixing
Gully gratings, being not dissimilar from manhole or inspection covers with drainage slots cast in them are fixed over a chamber in virtually the same way as manhole covers.

Siting
The siting of gulleys is dependant on the expected rainfall, the area to be drained, the capacity of the gully and the fall of the land.

For roads, the maximum spacing for gulleys is 45m.

Expect gratings to be partially blocked by dirt, debris and leaves when making calculations.

In paved areas, gulleys should be sited away from the major pedestrian flows which should preferably be along summits. As a rough guide, for paving at a slope of 1:100 (1%) gulleys should be sited at 20 m spacing.

As soon as any drainage scheme is envisaged the relevant specialists should be consulted.

Maintenance
Apart from routine cleaning and inspection, gulleys rarely require attention. Gratings which fracture (rare) should be replaced immediately.

Recommendations
Gulleys and gratings should be selected which will withstand the worst possible expected conditions of rainfall and loading.

They must not be sited in dangerous places, for example, on the kerb corners of sharp bends, in the centres of footpaths etc.

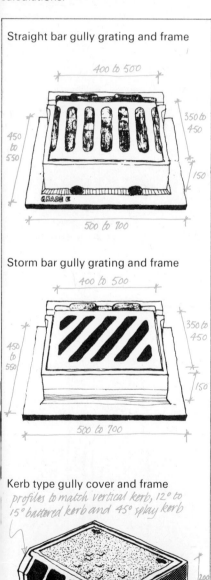

Straight bar gully grating and frame

400 to 500
350 to 450
450 to 550
150
500 to 700
GRASS B

Storm bar gully grating and frame

400 to 500
350 to 450
450 to 550
150
500 to 700

Kerb type gully cover and frame
profiles to match vertical kerb, 12° to 15° battered kerb and 45° splay kerb

200
550
450

3.3 Hydrants/ valves

Definitions and uses
Mains water has to be capable of being controlled, used and measured. This is accomplished by the use of valves, hydrants and meters usually contained in underground chambers along the mains supply pipe. The position of a chamber is indicated by means of a vertical marker-plate fixed to a special post or a nearby wall.

Valves and stop-cocks regulate the flow of water between fully open and shut. A stop-cock is a small valve which is usually used to control the water flow to domestic dwellings and small buildings.

Hydrants and standpipes each incorporate a valve and an outlet.

A hydrant is usually housed in an underground chamber and the outlet is threaded to accept a hose pipe;(a fire hydrant accepts a fire-hose),and the flow is controlled by the use of a removable long key which fits on to the valve spindle.

A standpipe is a tap on the end of a pipe about 1m above ground; it can be temporary or permanent. Temporary standpipes are usually screwed onto the hose outlets of hydrants whilst permanent standpipes are contained in insulated boxes with a door hinged for access. The tap outlet is often threaded to accept a hose pipe.

Meters are contained in chambers either on their own or combined with a stop tap.

Access to underground water chambers is by way of a hinged or removable lid or cover.

Materials and finishes
All water equipment has to conform to water board regulations in materials and finishes. Traditional materials: brass, copper, lead and iron are being augmented by stainless steel and plastics.

Chambers are generally made from brick or precast concrete.

Covers are made from cast iron, aluminium or precast concrete; they should have an anti-slip surface-pattern and contain a message to indicate what is underneath.

In addition, stop-cock chambers and covers can now be obtained in plastics and glass reinforced cement.

Construction and fixing
The size of chamber covers can vary between 150mm x 150mm and 600mm x 450mm; the depth will vary to suit the depth of the water main.

Siting

As with manhole/inspection covers (1.5) valve and hydrant covers are sited above their related water mains and often there is little room for manoeuvre along this line, for example, stop-cocks should be opposite their related dwellings. Nevertheless, care should be taken to site them so that they provide the minimum inconvenience when in use and the minimum danger when closed.

The frame and cover must be perfectly flush with the surrounding surfaces (true to falls) and sited at summits rather than valleys.

The indicator plates or posts should be sited vertically as close to the chamber as is practicable, without causing any obstruction or danger to passers by. The plates may have to be found quickly by emergency services unfamiliar with their exact location and so should face the road and not be camouflaged into their surroundings.

Maintenance

Stop-cock and water meter covers, being rarely used, seldom require maintenance. Outlet point covers, on the other hand, may be used very frequently and so must be kept clear of dirt and the hinges greased from time to time.

A cover should never be left in the open position unless it is surrounded by barriers, or a person is in attendance to divert road or foot traffic round it.

On closing, the cover must seat properly into the frame with no projection above ground level.

Recommendations

Always ensure that the cover/frames are strong enough to withstand the expected loads; if in doubt, assume the worst.

As covers/frames are, in the main, obligatory, little can be achieved environmentally with them except for careful siting and frame surround detailing.

In roads, leave at least 1m clear between frames and kerb.

Avoid siting covers/frames on sharp bends in roads carrying fast moving traffic.

Useful names (for addresses see chapter 21)
Bergo Ltd
Brooklyns Westbrick Ltd
Glasdon Ltd
Mono Concrete Ltd
John Needham & Sons Ltd

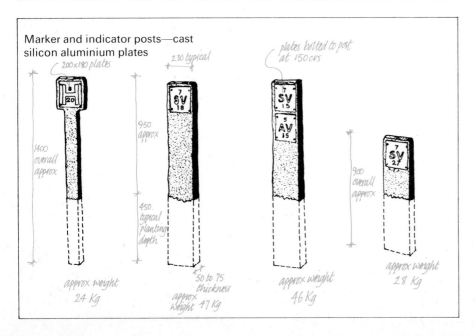

Precast concrete chambers and covers — all sections interlock

stopcock chamber

cast iron or plastic cover section 2

150 150

wall section heights 75, 100, 150, and 230

base blocks 150 or 230 high

190 190

hydrant chamber

600 450

top cover section height 100

wall section heights 75, 100 and 150

base wall section

base section

overall height varies to suit depth of water main

Marker and indicator posts—cast silicon aluminium plates

200x180 plates

230 typical

plates bolted to post at 150 crs

1400 overall approx

950 approx

450 typical planting depth

50 to 75 thickness

approx weight 24 Kg

approx weight 47 Kg

approx weight 46 Kg

900 overall approx

approx weight 28 Kg

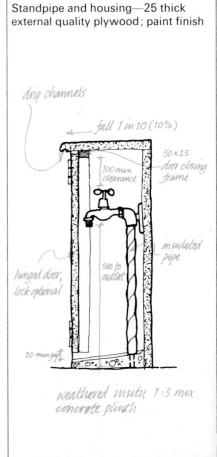

Standpipe and housing—25 thick external quality plywood; paint finish

drip channels

fall 1 in 10 (10%)

50 x 25 door closing frame

100 min clearance

insulated pipe

500 to outlet

hinged door, lock optional

20 min gap

weathered insitu 1:3 mix concrete plinth

24

3.4 Fountains/ drinking fountains

Definitions and uses

Moving water has inestimable value in the urban environment. It provides natural stimuli so often lacking in our over-designed urban surroundings.

A fountain consists of a submersible pump producing one or more upward facing jets or sprays of water either fixed or moving, and which are usually collected, after the effect of gravity, in a receptacle either on its own or as a series draining one to another.

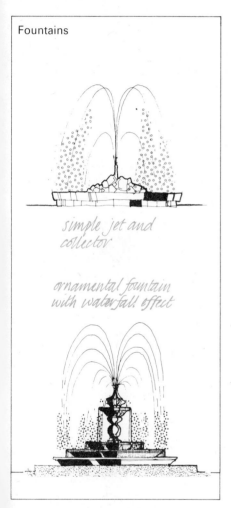

Fountains

simple jet and collector

ornamental fountain with waterfall effect

Fountains can vary from the most simple single jet of water pointing straight upwards to exceedingly complicated configurations of moving and pulsing spray patterns and decorated sculptural collectors.

The simpler the fountain, the more natural it is, and the more the effects of wind and natural light combine with it to form the overall effect.

At the other extreme, the most complicated fountains often combine coloured artificial lights with the water patterns to provide a show akin to a theatrical event.

Drinking fountains consist of a single jet of water which is mounted about 800mm high and which can be drunk 'en-route' to a collector.

Historically, drinking fountains were often a part of a horse-trough but nowadays they are used principally for humans to slake their thirst.

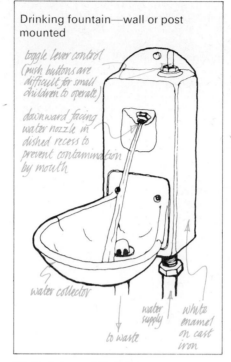

Drinking fountain—wall or post mounted

toggle lever control (push buttons are difficult for small children to operate)

downward facing water nozzle in dished recess to prevent contamination by mouth

water collector

water supply

to waste

white enamel on cast iron

Materials and finishes

The major constituents of a fountain are water jets and sprays produced by one or more submersible pumps.

The pumps are made from water resistant materials; copper, bronze, stainless steel, plastics etc and usually powered by electric motors.

The collectors are made from the above materials plus natural stone, cast iron, concrete etc. Collectors can be natural such as pools, ponds or lakes.

Drinking fountain collectors are made from enamelled cast iron or stainless steel with fittings in copper and chromed brass.

Requirements for a simple fountain

check that the foundations will support the weight of fountain and water (assume overflow to be blocked and water to run off collector)

collector impervious surround

mains electricity

water inlet and valve to regulate water level

overflow

submersible pump

Construction and fixing

Water 'en-masse' is very heavy (a pint of water weighs a pound and a quarter) so the limiting factor of most fountains is the weight of the collector and its water content. The chosen site must be capable of supporting this weight and also providing the services required, mains water and electricity, and occasional drainage.

Fountains and drinking fountains must be fixed securely so that concerted vandalism or high spirits have no untoward effect. The fountains in Trafalgar Square, London bear witness to the stimulating effect water has on people.

As fountains are so diverse, each fixing detail should be cleared by a Structural Engineer, unless it is used in an existing pool, pond, lake or the like.

Drinking fountains should be fixed at a height such that small children can use them ie 800mm high.

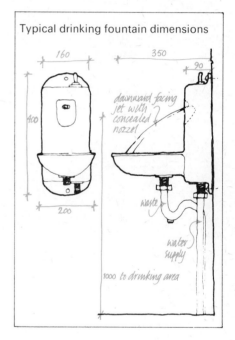

Typical drinking fountain dimensions

160   350   90

400

200

downward facing jet with concealed nozzle

waste

water supply

1000 to drinking area

Siting

A fountain, more than anything else, has to be related to its immediate surroundings. Should it be a dominant or sub-dominant feature? Should it be complicated or simple?

A fountain should not cause an unavoidable nuisance to passers by. A vertical jet can be blown considerable distances sideways in a strong wind (assume a fall angle of 45° from the top of the jet) and so provision must be made to allow avoidance of this splash area or to regulate the height of the jet in windy weather.

Footpaths surrounding fountains should generally be impervious and adequately drained.

Fountains can be quite noisy, and this factor should be considered before deciding on the type of fountain to use.

Drinking fountains can be free-standing, wall-mounted or even recessed into a wall.

They should not be sited so as to obstruct a footpath nor should they be hidden away out of sight. Remember that an adult bending over a drinking fountain sticks out some distance from the water source. The more prominent a drinking fountain is, the less likely it is to suffer from vandalism and neglect.

Maintenance
Simple fountains and drinking fountains require little maintenance other than the occasional ministrations of a plumber on a normal maintenance cycle.

The more complicated a fountain becomes, the more complicated and costly the maintenance and the higher the risk of malfunction.

Any collector will inevitably collect dirt and debris and should be cleaned frequently as a part of the regular street cleaning cycle.

Recommendations
If at all possible try to introduce moving water into environmental schemes.

Fountains enhance any area. The simplest of fountains can make seating areas and the like very successful and attractive. They can be the focal points of squares and small gardens and provide desirable oases in the urban environment.

Useful names (for addresses see chapter 21)
Edward Barber & Co Ltd
Brooklyns Westbrick Ltd
Concentric Fabrications Ltd
T A Harris Ltd
Mono Concrete Ltd
Ubbink-Telmrose Ltd

3.5 Canals/ aqueducts

Definitions and uses
Canals and aqueducts are man-made waterways.

Canals have a towing path (towpath) running along one or both of the banks.

Historically, canals were used for the transport of ships and boats carrying goods, but as most goods are now transported by road and rail, canals have become important for their amenity value and the opportunities they afford for recreation: wild life, fishing, boating and so on.

However, with the increase in road congestion and the recent escalations of fuel costs, there has been a revival of interest in canals as a means of transporting goods.

Aqueducts, in this manual, are small canals used only for the passage of water, though The British Waterways Board would define a water trough which carries boats over an obstruction as an aqueduct.

Canals and aqueducts can be used as a storm relief system. Rainwater is drained into canals and aqueducts which run into rivers, lakes and seas.

Canals may be pervious or impervious depending on the substrate.

Materials and finishes
Traditionally canals and aqueducts were lined with dry stone or brick walls or puddled clay but nowadays pre-cast concrete edge units or steel piles are assembled together to form a continuous wall, the base being in situ concrete or puddled clay.

For sloping banked canal sides Mono BG, or similar, slabs may be used filled with soil and seeded or planted. If it is necessary to make this lining impervious a puddled clay lining must be carried up under the slabs.

Towpaths are usually made from compacted gravel, hoggin, shale, cinders, natural stone or brick.

Construction and fixing
Bends in a canal should have a minimum inside radius of 3 times its width.

A minimum clearance of 1.8m should be allowed between the surface of the water and the underside of bridges, tunnels etc.

Aqueducts, used as surface water drainage features in pedestrian areas, also make very effective vehicle/pedestrian barriers.

Traditional canal construction

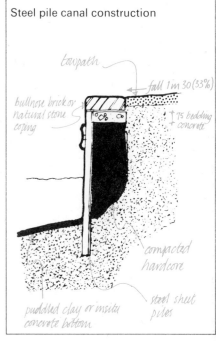

Steel pile canal construction

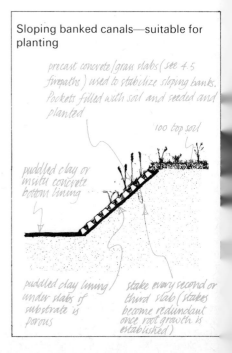

Sloping banked canals—suitable for planting

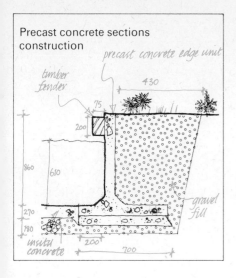

Precast concrete sections
construction

precast concrete edge unit

timber fender

430

75

200

860   610

270

180

insitu concrete   200   700   *gravel fill*

Siting

As canals and aqueducts are such a strong linear feature they will inevitably play a very dominant part in any scheme and the greatest care should be taken in siting and detailing.

Maintenance

Canal maintenance can be carried out both from the towpath and from the water itself. The cost varies enormously depending on the materials used and the depth and width of the canal.

Apart from the normal street cleaning cycle being extended to include water-cleaning, aqueduct maintenance is equivalent to that of kerb side drainage channels, which is virtually negligible.

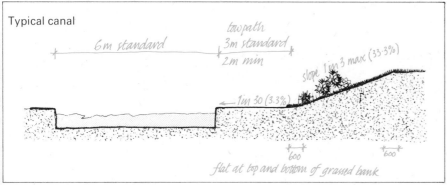

Typical canal

6 m standard   *towpath 3m standard 2m min*

slope 1 in 3 max (33·3%)

1 in 30 (3.3%)

600   600

flat at top and bottom of grassed bank

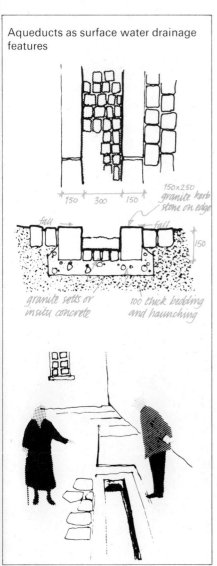

Aqueducts as surface water drainage features

150   300   150   *150x250 granite kerb stone on edge*

fall   *fall*   150

granite setts or insitu concrete   *100 thick bedding and haunching*

Recommendations

As for the previous subject, moving water has inestimable value in the urban environment and, though small, aqueducts can be a powerful element in any environmental scheme in addition to their use as surface water drainage channels.

Opportunities to build new canals, especially in the urban environment, are exceedingly limited, but wherever large developments are planned a canal can be a very useful linking element and an invaluable way of introducing nature into artificial surroundings.

Small aqueducts can be very usefully used in the dual function of surface/storm water drainage and vehicle/pedestrian separation. Though this practice is not generally to be found in England it is used extensively elsewhere in the world, particularly in Iran and Germany. However, a good historic example of this can be observed at Helston, Cornwall. It is interesting to observe that neither pedestrians nor vehicles make a habit of stepping or driving into aqueducts used in this way.

3.6 Ponds and pools

Ponds and pools are very desirable in the urban environment. They may occur naturally or be man made.

Traditionally in man made ponds and pools the lining was formed in puddled clay or concrete, but nowadays these have largely been replaced by polythene, pvc or butyl sheeting varying in thickness from 0.5 to 2mm.

Small pools may be emptied by syphoning with a hose pipe, but it is more practical if drainage is built in.

Many types of plants can be grown in, round and on ponds and pools. As with any planting, vandalism is most prevalent during the early years. Damaged plants should be replaced quickly and, wherever possible, temporary protection should be installed during this most vulnerable time.

If the pond is large enough it may be stocked with fish which will certainly please the local herons, cats and schoolboys.

On the whole, ponds enhance the urban environment and encourage the growth of interesting flora and fauna.

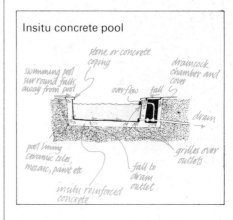

Insitu concrete pool

stone or concrete coping   *draincock chamber and cover*

swimming pool surround falls away from pool   *overflow*   *fall*

drain

pool lining ceramic tiles, mosaic, paint etc   *fall to drain outlet*   *grilles over outlets*

insitu reinforced concrete

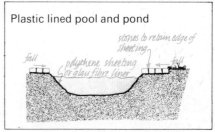

Plastic lined pool and pond

stones to retain edge of sheeting

fall   *polythene sheeting or glass fibre liner*   *fall*

Useful names (for addresses see chapter 21)
Atlas Stone Co Ltd
Du Pont (UK) Ltd

ROADS

Roads

Roads (vehicular pavements) are primarily designed to carry wheeled vehicles and must have a continuous, impervious hard surface.

The ideal road is wide enough to carry all the traffic wanting to use it and is absolutely safe and free of any type of hindrance.

In urban environments, where space is at a premium, the ideal road is seldom achieved, and a compromise must be accepted which attempts to reconcile many conflicting requirements such as vehicle movements in all directions at the same time, pedestrians crossing, vehicles crossing, vehicles stopping, vehicles parking, and so on.

Not only must all these factors be borne in mind, but as areas change so does the 'road use' of the roads linking these areas, and putting the right road, in the right place at the right time is fraught with difficulties, even at the best of times.

In actual fact, however, the long-suffering motorist is remarkably tolerant of the impositions heaped on him when travelling in an urban environment and, on the whole, accepts his lot with equanimity.

4.1 Concerning pollution

Road traffic unfortunately has an adverse effect on the environment and can constitute *the* major source of both air pollution and noise in urban areas. The worst affected areas are usually those in close proximity to roads. The extent of undesirable effects is markedly dependent upon the detailed layout of roads and its surroundings. 'Targets' for the pollution include people, animals, vegetation, buildings, and furnishings.

Exhaust emissions

Vehicle exhaust contains many pollutants. Those most commonly of concern are carbon monoxide, lead, hydrocarbons, oxides of nitrogen and smoke. Of these, carbon monoxide and nitrogen dioxide can have direct effects on health following inhalation. In most situations the concentrations of these two pollutants do not reach high enough levels to warrant concern, but this may not be true where, for example, heavy traffic or vehicle congested roads pass close to occupied premises, or shopping precincts.

Lead is a more insidious pollutant for several reasons. One is that it is a cumulative poison which affects the nervous system. Another is that it can enter the body, not only by the inhalation of exhaust fumes, but also via contaminated food crops grown close to busy roads. In the case of children, another, and perhaps more important route to the body, is by the accidental ingestion of lead-contaminated street dust.

As far as smoke is concerned, the most obvious effects accrue from its role as a soiling agent. In modern cities where motor vehicles are the main mode of transportation, smoke emissions by motor vehicles can constitute the major source of this pollutant. Accumulated smoke from vehicles is very black, especially from diesel engines, and is a major contributor to the dirtying of clothes, and exteriors and interiors of buildings.

Hydrocarbons from vehicles may also contribute to soiling. This is probably most easily observed from the thin films of grease which can be found on the windows and paintwork of buildings adjacent to busy roads. For pedestrians, the odour of aldehydes may represent an unpleasant and nauseating experience.

Noise

The problem of noise in urban areas is widespread and in many cases is very severe, and traffic noise in particular is one of the major offenders.

In a national survey on aspects of the environment, 89% of the interviewees said that they could hear traffic noise in their homes, and 23% said that they were bothered by it. Virtually every dwelling is built adjacent to a road but it is the volume of traffic using the road which will determine the extent of the noise problem. Even a modest feeder road to a residential area can cause a noise problem, while properties adjacent to a major road will be severely affected. Individual members of the public have very different sensitivity and response to traffic noise. Some people are annoyed by a single vehicle while others find the noise from a major road completely acceptable. Despite this, most guidance available is based on some form of average response.

Visual intrusion and inconvenience

The obvious undesirable effects of air pollution and noise from vehicles are not the only ones to consider. The sight of moving vehicles, during day or night, can also be psychologically disturbing, especially where people are attempting to relax. Badly sited car parks, detract from the visual appearance and amenity value of otherwise attractive areas. Pedestrians and cyclists have difficulty in crossing busy roads and certainly experience delay and frustration in going from one place to another.

Designing to minimise the effects of pollution

In general the aim must be to site busy roads away from places where people spend a lot of their time, such as homes, offices, schools and recreation areas. Because of pressure to use land, however, it is often not possible to allow as much separation as might ideally be desired. Thus, in locations where space is at a premium, it becomes necessary to make technical calculations of the noise and pollution levels. These can then be compared with accepted guideline values for noise and air pollution, which would themselves depend upon the type of exposure being guarded against. For example, noise levels in bedrooms would generally have to meet a more stringent guideline than that for a playground. Conversely, lead in playgrounds might reasonably be expected to be of more concern than in, say, a car park. Unfortunately the complexity of these situations means that simple rules are not available to cover the multitude of diverse situations which can arise. In cases where it is thought that there might be a risk to health or a serious loss of amenity, expert scientific advice should be sought. However, it is useful to be aware of some of the types of options which have been considered and used in the past. The remainder of this section will outline some examples of these.

Trees and planting

It is generally accepted that screens of trees or bushes do not reduce noise levels very much, although they may have a small effect in reducing the air pollution impact of the road. The main benefit of planting trees and shrubs, and landscaping areas between a road and adjacent housing, is likely to be psychological in that it provides a visual barrier between the dwellings and the road, and so, wherever remotely possible, planting and landscaping should be introduced into the environment.

Mounds

A more certain beneficial effect can usually be obtained by incorporating earth mounds into landscaping of the road margins in such a way as to act as a noise and visual barrier. (See 1.7 Mounds) For a mound to be effective as a noise barrier it must be high enough to block the line-of-sight from the far carriageway to the target, which may be, for example, an upper-storey bedroom window.

Screen barriers

Where there is insufficient space for earth mounds a screen type of noise barrier can be used which, depending on the detailed geometry of the situation, can give noise reductions of up to about 10 to 20 dB(A). Barriers of this type do not have to be massive as the limiting factor is likely to be noise passing over them, rather than through them. For a designed barrier 2 metres high, a mass of 10 kg/m² is normally sufficient. The maximum effect is achieved when the barrier is sited as close as is possible to the source of the noise.

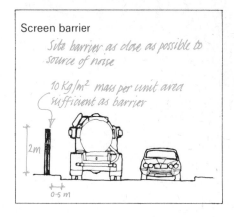

Screen barrier

Site barrier as close as possible to source of noise

10 kg/m² mass per unit area sufficient as barrier

2m

0·5 m

Roads in-cut

Earth mounds and screen barriers cannot protect high rise buildings. Even roads in-cut do not provide protection from noise to the upper floors of high rise buildings very close to the road.

In some cities this problem has been tackled by partially enclosing the top of the road in-cut, but this is an expensive option which may bring about other problems by 'channelling' the exhaust emissions to places where they form localised high concentrations.

New buildings near busy roads

Many new buildings are built adjacent to busy main roads and urban motorways. In such cases it is possible to design against pollution. A single-aspect screen block should be built along the entire length of that part of the development that flanks the roadway. Rooms facing the road should be those which are least sensitive to noise and visual intrusion and should be either glazed with at least 12mm thick glass fixed-lights, or have double windows. This may require the inclusion of artificial ventilation. If so, air inlets to the ventilation system of the screen block should be sited on the facade of the building away from the road in order to draw on less-polluted air.

In addition to the reduction of noise levels, the screen block should reduce air pollution and noise in the area within the development. It has been found in

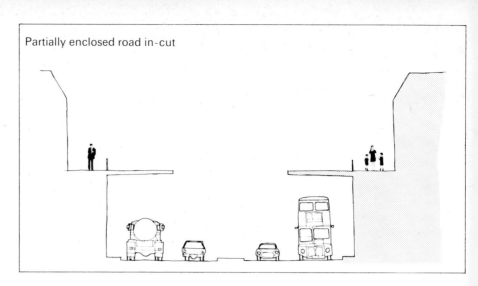

Partially enclosed road in-cut

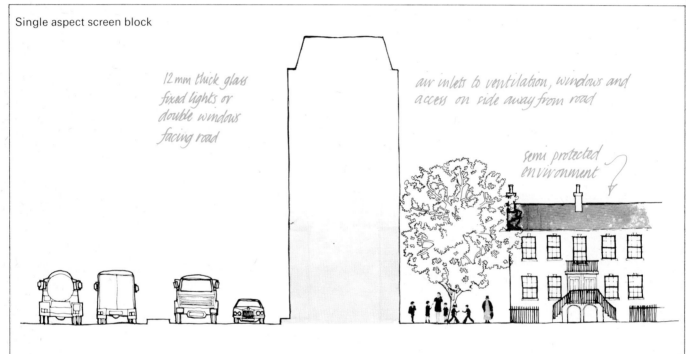

Single aspect screen block

12mm thick glass fixed lights or double windows facing road

air inlets to ventilation, windows and access on side away from road

semi protected environment?

some cases that the airborne lead concentrations on the side away from the road were roughly half those on the side adjacent to the road, and that low rise buildings within the development did not require additional noise insulation.

New buildings near lightly-used roads
In this situation quite minor changes in layout can bring about a marked reduction in nuisance from road traffic pollution.

Land Compensation Act grants
Under this Act the responsible authority may acquire land by agreement for the purpose of mitigating any adverse effect which the existence or use of any public work has or will have on the surroundings. This may include, for example, the acquisition of land for the planting of trees, shrubs or plants of any description and the laying out of areas of grassland. Costs arising in this way can be included in the overall cost of a road project, and may therefore be covered by Government grant.

Not this

play space separated from buildings by road

footpath adjacent to road and on wrong side of road

buildings

playspace

footpath

road

garden

But this

soft mound and trees separating footpath and building from road

buildings shielding playspaces and gardens from road and footpath

road

footpath

playspace and garden

lower floors shielded from road noise and visual intrusion by mound upper floors shielded by trees

New Housing grants

The Department of the Environment recognise that additional costs can be involved in protecting new housing against pollution from road vehicles. Local authorities can apply for an additional ad hoc allowance to the 'housing cost yardstick' which is the limit imposed by the Government on the costs of building new housing, and this addition can be used for such measures as the provision of 'buffer zone' landscaping; earth-mound barriers, tree screens, double-glazing, single aspect dwellings and so on. The ad hoc allowance normally amounts to an increase of up to 7% in the yardstick. The precise percentage is calculated on a pro-rata basis from the area of the site affected by L10 noise levels of 68 dB(A) and above. Where a noisy road is to the South of a proposed site, single-aspect dwellings would face North and in this case the development may qualify for double the ad hoc grant, that is, up to the maximum addition of 14%.

4.2 Construction

Whilst the design of roads is best left to specialists, road and traffic engineers, sufficient information is given in this manual for the user to have some idea as to the requirements for roads, which are, after all, a very dominant feature in the urban environment.

The summit, along the centre of a road, and the kerbs should be laid true to bone: the calculated level of the road. The road is laid to fall to gullies having a maximum spacing of 45m.

If no reinforcement is used expansion joints are needed at intervals of about 5m.

In continuously reinforced concrete, heavy reinforcement is laid without breaks and there are no slab joints.

Sub-bases are usually granular materials alone or granular materials stabilised with cement.

Road Base materials include: graded crushed stone, single-size stone filled with fines, lean mix concrete, cement-based granular base or bituminous granular materials using bitumen or tar as binder.

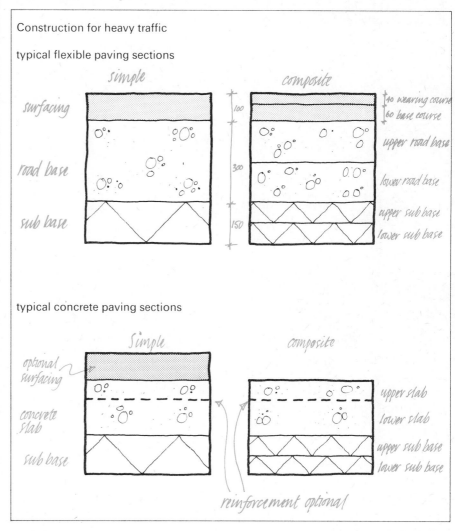

Construction for heavy traffic

typical flexible paving sections

typical concrete paving sections

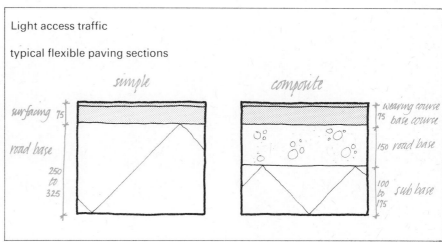

Light access traffic

typical flexible paving sections

Light access traffic

typical concrete paving section

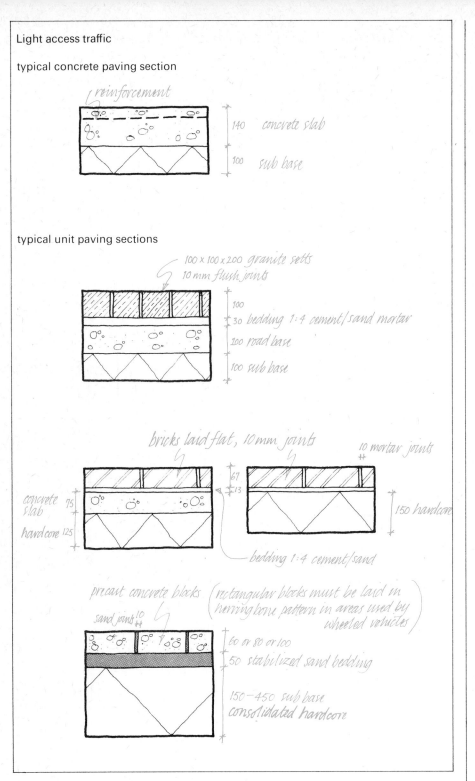

reinforcement

140 concrete slab

100 sub base

typical unit paving sections

100 x 100 x 200 granite setts
10 mm flush joints

100
30 bedding 1:4 cement/sand mortar
100 road base
100 sub base

bricks laid flat, 10 mm joints

10 mortar joints

concrete slab 75
hardcore 125

67
13

150 hardcore

bedding 1:4 cement/sand

precast concrete blocks (rectangular blocks must be laid in
sand joints 10   herring bone pattern in areas used by
                              wheeled vehicles)

60 or 80 or 100
50 stabilized sand bedding

150–450 sub base
consolidated hardcore

Primary distributor road widths

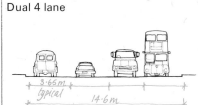

Dual 4 lane

3·65 m typical   14·6 m

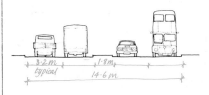

Dual 4 lane with central refuges

3·2 m typical   1·8 m   14·6 m

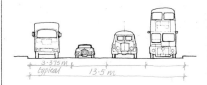

Single 4 lane

3·375 m typical   13·5 m

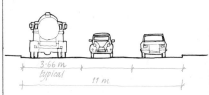

Dual 3 lane

3·66 m typical   11 m

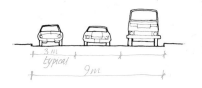

Single 3 lane (only for tidal flows)

3 m typical   9 m

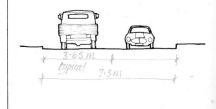

Dual 2 lane

3·65 m typical   7·3 m

District distributor road widths

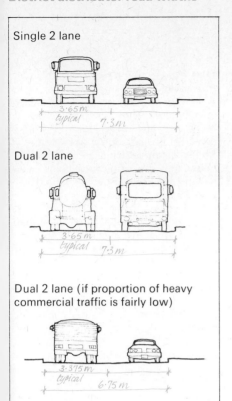

Single 2 lane

3·65 m typical
7·3 m

Dual 2 lane

3·65 m typical
7·3 m

Dual 2 lane (if proportion of heavy commercial traffic is fairly low)

3·375 m typical
6·75 m

Local distributor road widths

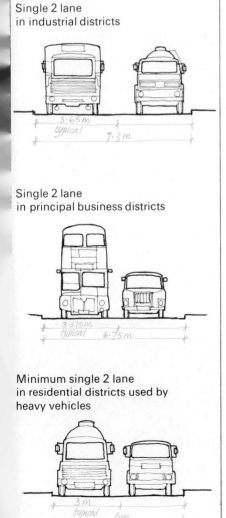

Single 2 lane in industrial districts

3·65 m typical
7·3 m

Single 2 lane in principal business districts

3·375 m typical
6·75 m

Minimum single 2 lane in residential districts used by heavy vehicles

3 m typical
6 m

Access road widths

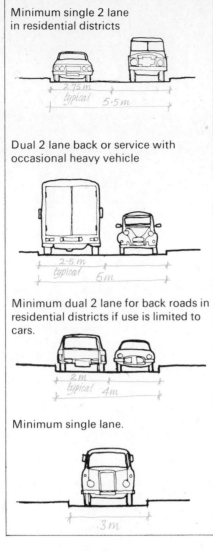

Minimum single 2 lane in residential districts

2·75 m typical
5·5 m

Dual 2 lane back or service with occasional heavy vehicle

2·5 m typical
5 m

Minimum dual 2 lane for back roads in residential districts if use is limited to cars.

2 m typical
4 m

Minimum single lane.

3 m

Lay-by and bus bay widths

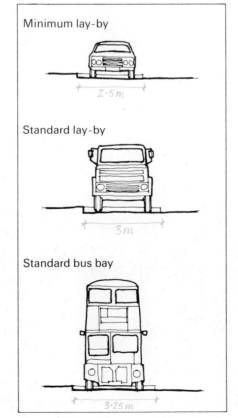

Minimum lay-by

2·5 m

Standard lay-by

3 m

Standard bus bay

3·25 m

Parking layouts

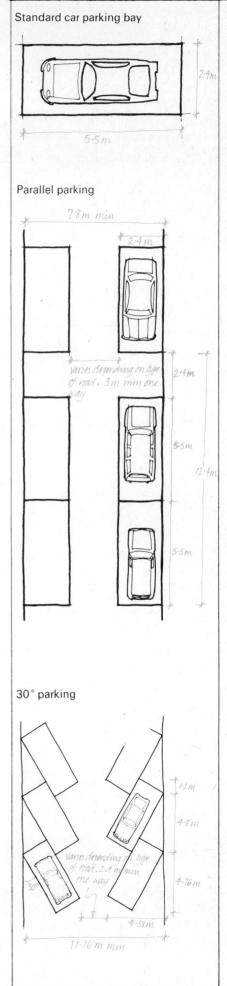

Standard car parking bay

2·4 m
5·5 m

Parallel parking

7·8 m min
2·4 m
varies depending on type of road. 3 m min one way
2·4 m
5·5 m
12·4 m
5·5 m

30° parking

1·2 m
4·8 m
varies depending on type of road. 2·4 m min one way
30°
4·76 m
4·38 m
11·16 m min

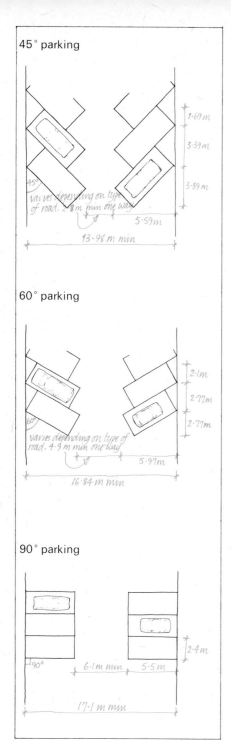

45° parking

1·69 m
3·39 m
3·89 m
45°
varies depending on type
of road. 2·8 m min one way
5·59 m
13·98 m min

60° parking

2·1 m
2·77 m
2·77 m
60°
varies depending on type of
road. 4·9 m min one way
5·97 m
16·84 m min

90° parking

2·4 m
90°
6·1 m min
5·5 m
17·1 m min

Junction layouts
showing minimum dimensions

A 10m radius will allow large vehicles to turn without hindrance to other traffic on the through road at 6.75m width but there will be slight interference with the traffic on the 5.5m width stem road.

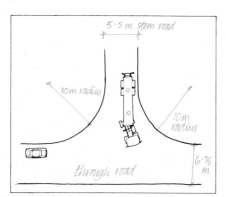

5·5 m stem road
10m radius
10m radius
through road
6·75 m

A 5m radius allows large vehicles to turn into and out of the junction by using most of the width of both roads. This radius can only be used where traffic is very light.

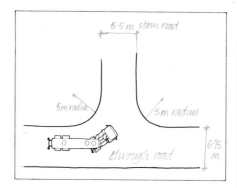

5·5 m stem road
5m radius
5m radius
through road
6·75 m

A sharp corner, 500mm radius quadrant, will discourage any turning. To prevent vehicles cutting the corner by mounting the kerb, a strategically sited tree or substantial bollard can be highly effective: for siting see 1.3 and 8.2.

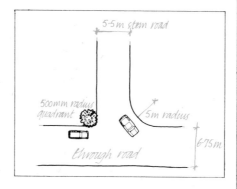

5·5 m stem road
500mm radius quadrant
5m radius
through road
6·75 m

Turning ends
Dimension suitable for large vehicles

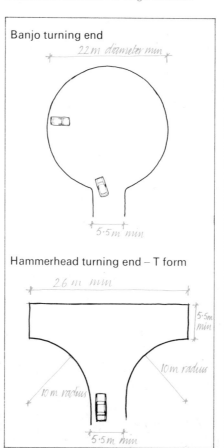

Banjo turning end

22 m diameter min
5·5 m min

Hammerhead turning end – T form

26 m min
5·5 m min
10 m radius
10 m radius
5·5 m min

4.4 Road markings/studs

Definitions and uses
Road markings are lines, dashes, squares or arrows painted or stuck onto road surfaces. They direct or advise traffic by centre lining, lane demarcation and edge marking etc. Road marking is also used to delineate boundaries, crossings, areas for parking and so on. Road markings can be reflective or non-reflective.

Road studs are set into or onto the road to emphasise road markings. They are made from metal, rubber or plastic; with reflective or non-reflective surfaces.

Traffic Sign Regulations lay down when and where markings and/or studs should be used – see Traffic Signs Manual.

Materials and finishes
Road marking materials are thermoplastic or spray resin or paint or self adhesive plastic tape or plastic tiles fixed with epoxy adhesive. On public roads colours are restricted to white for general use and yellow for restrictions. Other colours of self-adhesive plastic tape are available including red, orange, green, blue, purple, brown and black. These can be used for marking out sports areas and private roads.

Tapes are also available in British Standard oblique stripes; black/yellow, black/white, red/white and green/white.

For use in the dark, the resin, paint and tapes have small 'ballotini' glass beads added to the mix or to the surface coating.

Non-reflective studs were traditionally made from stainless steel which is self polishing and bright but can lead to skidding in wet conditions.

Plastic tiles and studs are sometimes used to mark out pedestrian crossings instead of paint or resin (see 13.2).

Reflective road studs, having been for so long synonymous with the classic 'catseyes' (a Yorkshireman's invention) made from cast iron and rubber with silvered glass lenses, are now being made from more modern materials, ABS (Acrylonitrile Butadiene Styrene) plastic and rubber/fabric combinations.

Reflective lenses are available in white, red, yellow and green.

Construction and fixing
Thermoplastic resin and paints can be screeded, sprayed or brushed directly on to most paving materials although a tack coat is occasionally recommended for use on concrete.

The film thickness of the resin or paint is 1.5mm, which does not induce skidding, but as, in practice, markings are renewed by overpainting, the thicknesses can build up 3, 4.5, 6mm etc and can actually promote skidding, particularly for bicycles in wet conditions. The effect is not unlike the one which used to be provoked by tram lines.

Minute reflective glass beads can be premixed with the paint or resin or dropped on to freshly laid top surfaces.

For increased resistance to skidding calcined flint can be premixed with resin in the same way as glass beads.

These paints and resins are usually applied by machines at single line widths from 50–300mm and double line widths from 50–150mm.

For temporary markings, plastic tapes may be used. These are self adhesive and pressure sensitive, 0.6mm thick, with a metal base and abrasion resistant surface to withstand heavy traffic.

They can be applied by hand or machine to any dry, dirt-free paving materials, 5 minutes after an application of a primer to seal the surface.

If it should be necessary to remove the tape from the road surface, heating it with a blowlamp will allow it to be peeled off. Tape, therefore, is very suitable for marking temporary or experimental schemes which may require several changes to be made to them.

Tape is available in widths of 50, 100, 150 and 200mm.

Non reflective road studs are generally 50, 100 or 120mm diameter stainless steel or plastic.

It is desirable for studs to be slightly domed, about 15 to 20mm, to administer slight 'bumps' to the driver of a vehicle passing over them. This reminds him that he is changing lanes or, if the studs are marking the edge of a road, something worse.

Reflective road studs can have glass lenses incorporated into the body or can be completely covered with reflective beads. They are usually 100 or 120mm diameter with the exception of the original 'catseyes' which are oblong and variable in size, depending on the location.

Rubber studs are flexible and designed to clean the lenses as they are run over.

Plastic studs are generally rigid.

The studs are fixed either by the body or central shaft being mechanically inserted into the road surfacing material or stuck onto the road surface with hot

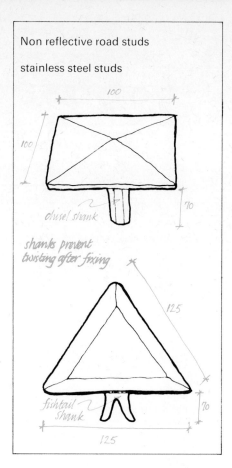

Non reflective road studs

stainless steel studs

chisel shank

shanks prevent twisting after fixing

fishtail shank

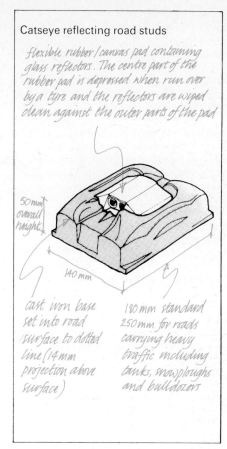

Catseye reflecting road studs

flexible rubber/canvas pad containing glass reflectors. The centre part of the rubber pad is depressed when run over by a tyre and the reflectors are wiped clean against the outer parts of the pad

50mm overall height

140mm

cast iron base set into road surface to dotted line (14mm projection above surface)

180mm standard 250mm for roads carrying heavy traffic including tanks, snowploughs and bulldozers

melting adhesive or epoxy adhesive. The road surface should be dry and free from dirt or grease at the time of application.

Siting
For the siting and dimensions of road markings and the siting of studs see the relevant Ministry of Transport regulations.

Maintenance
Road markings and studs are, in the main, obligatory, and so as they become worn, obliterated or damaged they should be reinstated without delay.

Recommendations
On public roads, road markings and studs have to be put in very specific positions, with very little digression possible: see the relevant Ministry of Transport instruments and regulations.

In pedestrian, historic and conservation areas, road markings should be used as sparingly as possible. In these areas, the yellow line width may be reduced to 50mm and a more discreet shade of yellow used (BS 381C no 310 Primrose or 353 Deep Cream) This provides a useful softening of the visual impact, particularly that of continuous double yellow lines.

Useful names (for addresses see chapter 21)
Amerace-Esna Ltd
Berger Traffic Marking Ltd
Gydelite Ltd
3M Company Ltd
Mor-Line Road Markers Ltd
Reflecting Roadstuds Ltd
Sportsmark Ltd

Non reflective road studs

plastic studs

15–20 typical

60·100·120 diameter typical

Reflective road studs

moulded plastic with glass reflector inserts

100·120 diameter typical

15–20 typical

glass bead covered

flat shaft prevents twisting

4.5 Firepaths

Firepaths are hard surfaced roads designed to carry emergency vehicles and their associated apparatus, fire engines, fire pumps, turntable ladders, ambulances, police cars etc.

A firepath must not be used by vehicles other than emergency vehicles. To prevent unauthorised access, gates are sometimes sited at the ends, secured by standard fire service padlocks.

Firepaths are 3m wide but may broaden out as necessary; near buildings for example.

Any hard surface material which can withstand the weight of several parked fire engines may be used: see 4.2 roads, heavy traffic. Care must be taken to ensure that the material is non-skid when wet: where there are fire engines, there is often a lot of surface water.

In grassed areas, firepaths can be constructed by using precast concrete slabs, in the form of a grid made up of concrete castellations, and regularly spaced soil bearing pockets in which grass may be seeded. The surface area comprises 25% concrete and 75% grass and the slabs are self-draining.

Grassed area firepath slab units are laid dry in regular rows on prepared foundations, and firmed into place.

Firepaths in grassed areas may be constructed in parallel tracks with a central strip of grass which may contain shallow services.

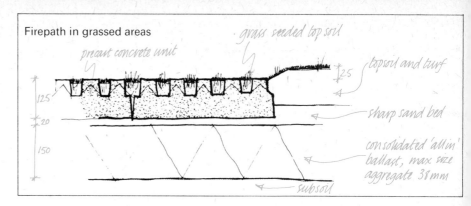

Firepath in grassed areas

grass seeded top soil
precast concrete unit
topsoil and turf
sharp sand bed
consolidated 'all in' ballast, max size aggregate 38mm
subsoil

125 / 125 / 20 / 150

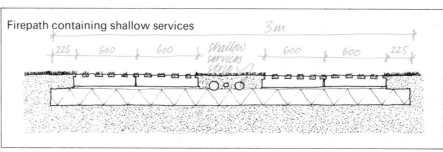

Firepath containing shallow services

3m

225 / 600 / 600 / shallow services strip / 600 / 600 / 225

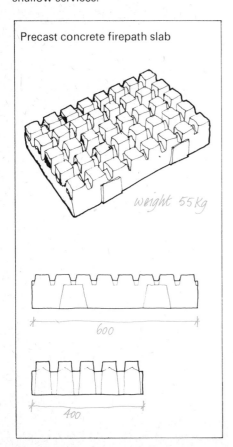

Precast concrete firepath slab

weight 55 kg

600

400

Siting

Before siting a firepath, consult the local Fire Brigade and Police, who will advise on preferred access points and directions (for example, access may be required only for wheeled escape ladders and hose pipes and not fire engines) or where facades should not be obstructed by trees, etc.

Hydrants (see 3.3) may have to be sited in conjunction with firepaths.

In places where a firepath runs through an area of hard surfacing in a pedestrian zone, the edges must be clearly defined so that fire engines will not stray onto areas which may not have sufficient foundations to support their weight. Such edges can be marked by trees, bollards, planters, planting beds etc or by a change in surface; colour, texture or material.

Maintenance

For maintenance of hard surfaces see 1.1 and 1.2, in situ and unit paving.

In grassed firepaths, the precast concrete slab/grass units can be treated as any other area of grass. Mowing should be carried out diagonally across the slabs until the turf is well established after which time it can be in any direction.

For approximate laid costs see 1.1 and 1.2, in situ and unit paving, including grassed area slab units.

Recommendations

Consult the Fire Brigade and Police at the earliest possible opportunity if a firepath is likely to be needed in any scheme: much abortive work can be avoided.

In grassed areas, firepaths can be very intrusive. Concrete/grass units provide a successful way of introducing firepaths into such areas.

Useful names (for addresses see chapter 21)
Mono Concrete Ltd

FOOTPATHS/
CYCLETRACKS/
STEPS/RAMPS/
STEPPED RAMPS

Footpaths/ cycletracks/ steps/ramps/ stepped ramps

Footpaths (footways) are normally hard surfaced, as they are designed to carry pedestrians over ground into which they might possibly sink up to their ankles, or further, in wet weather.

Footpaths adjoining roads are colloquially called 'pavements' which is a shortened version of 'pedestrian pavements'.

Cycle tracks, similarly, are designed to carry cyclists over the same type of ground.

Steps are used where slopes are too steep for a footpath to be safely negotiated by normal pedestrians ie anything steeper than 1 in 12 (8.3%). Each step should be at least large enough to accommodate a size 54 shoe (Old English size 14) in the direction of travel.

Steps may or may not need a handrail. If the vertical drop at the side of the steps exceeds 600mm, a handrail must be provided.

Ramps are short lengths of footpaths, which change levels up to a maximum slope of 1 in 12 (8.3%).

Stepped ramps are used on ground slopes of between 1 in 12 (8.3%) and 1 in 4 (25%). The ramp going has a constant slope of 1 in 12 (8.3%) and the riser height is varied to suit the slope of the ground.

Footpaths having slight curves are far more interesting to pedestrians than straight ones, particularly if they are sloped as well.

Wherever possible, it is the policy of the Greater London Council to separate pedestrian routes from roads. This can be accomplished by providing traffic-free pedestrian precincts, continuous overhead walkway systems, and so on.

Where roads must be crossed by pedestrians, and it is not feasible to provide a separated continuous pedestrian walkway, crossings should be provided.

The order of preference for road crossing is:

1   pedestrian crossing at ground level: see 13.2

2   subways: see 9.1

3   footbridges: see 10

5.1 Construction

As with roads, footpaths can be simple or composite.

They can be constructed from any insitu or unit-paving material (see 1.1 and 1.2) though obviously cost will have a great bearing on the materials selected.

In siting cycle tracks beware of blind corners near buildings and other obstructions to sight lines.

Recommended falls

Pre-cast concrete paving slabs:
1 in 30 (33%) maximum
1 in 72 (1.4%) minimum

Bricks, Setts and Blocks:
1 in 60 (1.6%)

Bituminous surfaces:
1 in 40 (2.5%) cross falls
1 in 200 (0.5%) long falls
1 in 60 (1.6%) maximum on playgrounds.

Footpaths and pavements

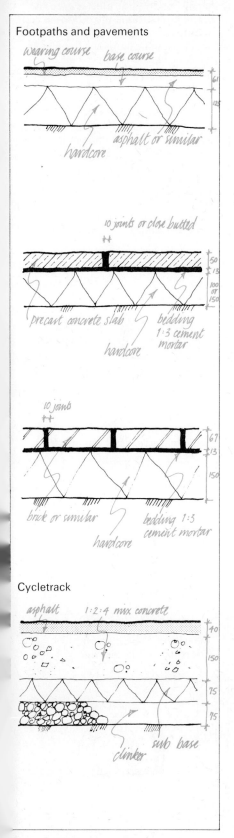

Cycletrack

Steps

precast paving slabs

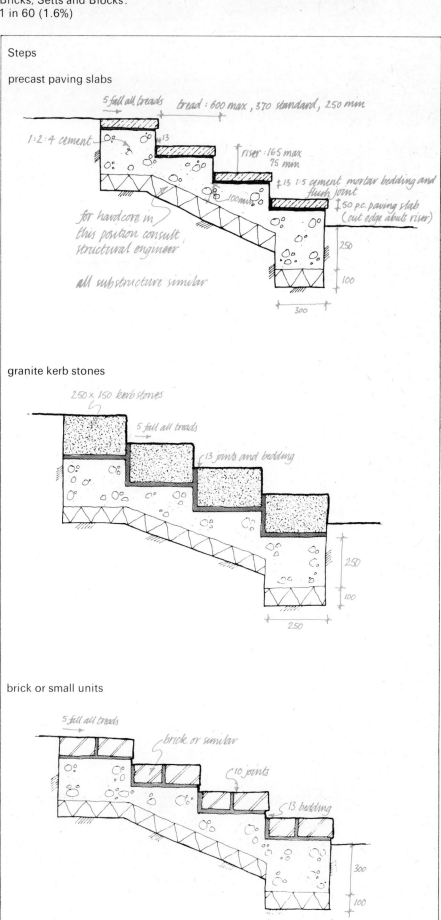

granite kerb stones

brick or small units

Ramps

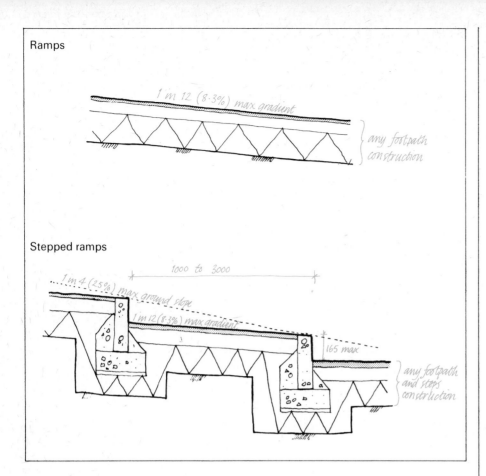

1 m 12 (8·3%) max gradient

} any footpath construction

Stepped ramps

1000 to 3000

1 m 4 (25%) max around slope

1 m 12 (8·3%) max gradient

165 max

} any footpath and steps construction

5.2 Siting and widths

The most difficult and neglected aspect of footpath design is deciding on the right place for the footpath. All too often one sees a beautifully constructed but unused footpath stretching away into the distance, with muddy tracks leading off and across it at various intervals.

If at all possible, the ideal way to site footpaths is to leave the proposed area of footpaths as grass or flattened earth for at least three months, after which time it will be patently obvious exactly where people want to go and with what frequency.

In new housing estates it may well be cheaper in the long run to delay the footpath contract for three months after

Typical widths of footpaths, pavements, steps, ramps

adjoining shops

3·5 m to 4·5 m clear   0·5 m min

adjoining principal business and industrial area distributor roads

3m clear   0·5 m min

in residential areas and beside industrial area access roads

2 m to 2·5 m clear   0·5 m min
1·8 m absolute min

the houses are occupied, before siting the footpaths. This avoids having unused footpaths and another contract to build extra footpaths later.

If it is absolutely impossible to site footpaths the ideal way, then an educated guess, and it can be no more than that, will have to be made as to the position of a new footpath. Remember that people tend to walk in straight lines and take the shortest possible route to their objective, unless they are physically prevented from doing so – knee high rails frequently have well used tracks formed behind them.

As cyclists generally travel for greater distances than pedestrians, small detours are not such anathema to them and a cyclist will tend to choose a route which is smooth, relatively level and continuous rather than the shortest possible distance between two points. However, cyclists should be thought of

as long distance pedestrians rather than small road vehicles.

The size of footpaths, cycletracks and steps is dependent on the type, volume and frequency of use. The worst expected case should be chosen when deciding on construction and width.

Once the clear width has been established, remember to add on space for lighting columns, traffic signs, traffic-signals, control boxes, seating, litter-bins etc. 1m will accommodate most obstructions, with the exception of seating which requires 2.5m minimum.

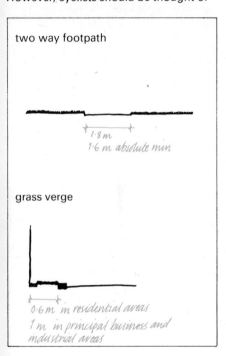

two way footpath

1·8 m
1·6 m absolute min

grass verge

0·6 m in residential areas
1 m in principal business and industrial areas

Typical widths of cycletracks
maximum gradient 1 in 20 (5%)
crossfalls 1 in 40 (2.5%)

one way

2·75 m standard
1·8 m min

two way

3·6 m standard

5.3 Recommend-
ations

Footpaths/cycletracks/steps can be made very interesting.

Slight curves are more interesting than straight lines; slopes are more interesting than level expanses; small units are more interesting and more sympathetic to the human scale than large slabs; colour can be used to brighten up a dull area: conversely grey can be used to tie together disparate colours and elements.

Footpaths can be a very strong element in the urban environment and great care must be taken in their design and detailing.

Within the overall design of the footpath, be it formal or informal, small unit patterns can be used to good effect.

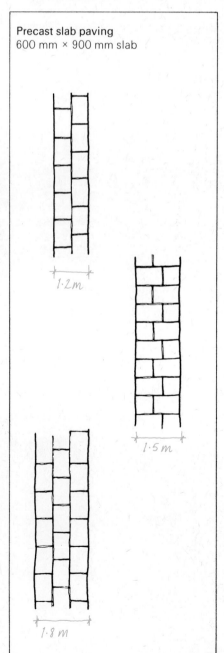

Precast slab paving
600 mm × 900 mm slab

1·2 m

1·5 m

1·8 m

43

Brick and block paving

stretcher bond along path   stretcher bond across path   basket weave pattern   herringbone pattern

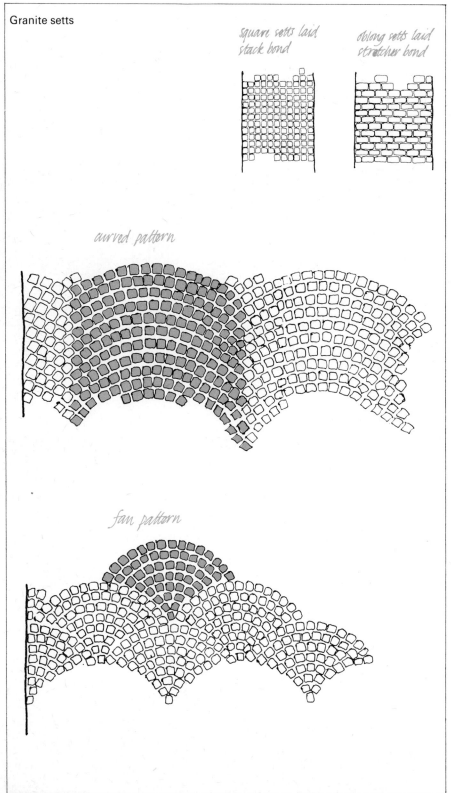

Granite setts

square setts laid stack bond   oblong setts laid stretcher bond

curved pattern

fan pattern

5.4 Escalators/travelators

Brief mention can be made of escalators and travelators. In the Greater London area, experimental schemes to introduce them into the open air have met with little success. The sheer mechanical complexities of moving people up and down on escalators or along travelators seem to multiply a thousand-fold once rain and wind and weather get to work.

In areas with high rates of vandalism, escalators and travelators make a very alluring and vulnerable target and are relatively easy to immobilise. An escalator out of action is more hazardous than a normal flight of steps.

If money is no object and there is constant supervision, escalators and travelators can save a considerable amount of pedestrian energy and time. If limitless money or constant supervision is absent, then it may well be best if the escalators and travelators are also absent.

Useful names (for addresses see chapter 21)
Dunlop Ltd
Marryat & Scott Ltd
Otis Elevator Co Ltd

KERBS/
MOWING STRIPS/
ISLANDS

Kerbs/ mowing strips/ islands

Kerbs are very versatile and have a multiplicity of uses.

To define edges of areas (pavement/grass/road).

To act as small retaining walls.

To form stairs (see 5.3.)

To act as physical barriers (vehicle/pedestrian).

To aid water drainage (form one side of a channel).

Urban kerbs
In urban areas and heavy traffic situations a kerb should be used which dissuades vehicles from driving over it.

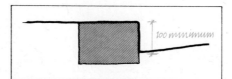

Semi-Rural kerbs
In semi-rural areas and light traffic situations mountable kerbs should be used. These avoid 'kerb shyness' and enable vehicles to leave the road in an emergency.

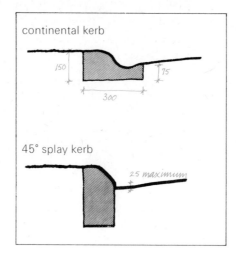

continental kerb

45° splay kerb

Radius kerbs
There are internal and external kerbs depending upon which surface is next to the road.

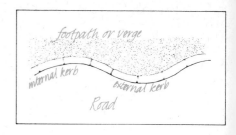

Generally, kerbs are used either on flat (preferred) or on edge. To use them on end can lead to problems.

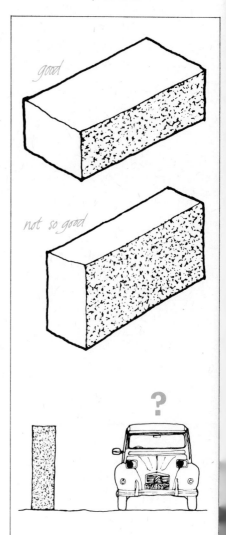

6.1 Natural stone kerbs/ quadrants

These are made from rocks classified as basalt, gabbro, granite and porphyry. There are many finishes from which to choose, at the most basic 'left rough' (cut to basic shape but left undressed) and the other extreme 'dressed and polished'. Any finishing operation adds cost.

For most purposes BS dressing 'B' will suffice 'fair picked, single axed or ridged'. Only the stone surface which is visible needs to be finished.

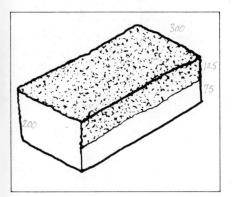

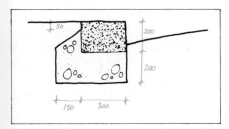

The sizes of straight edge and flat kerbs are:

Flat kerbs

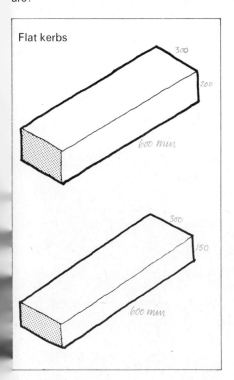

Flat kerbs

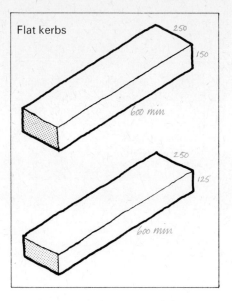

Edge kerbs

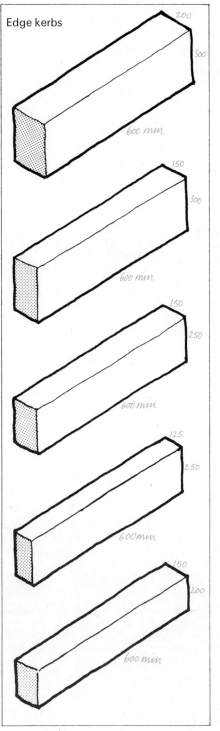

Quadrants should match the kerb against which they fit, in dimensions, material and finish.

There are two types of British Standard quadrants, type X and type Y.

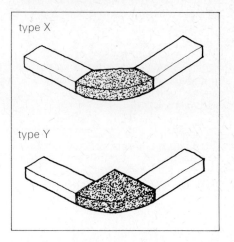

type X

type Y

Maintenance
Natural stone is generally very hardwearing and maintenance costs are negligible.

Comparative costs
Existing reworked granite – expensive
Second hand granite – expensive
New granite – very expensive

Recommendations
Where vehicles frequently hit or mount kerbs, granite should be used. It wears well and can be re-used or dressed in situ. It provides a high quality finish not found in other commonly used kerb materials.

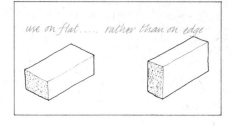

use on flat...... rather than on edge

6.2 Concrete kerbs

Standard concrete kerbs and quadrants are precast in grey concrete and the finish is ex-mould.

Colour may be introduced by using cement pigments or by exposing the aggregate, but any deviation from the standard will increase costs – see 1.2 Materials and Finishes.

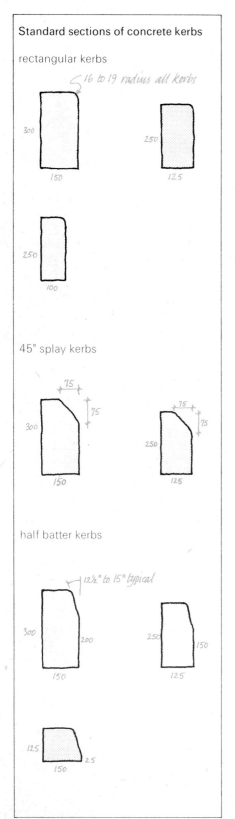

Standard sections of concrete kerbs

rectangular kerbs

16 to 19 radius all kerbs

300 / 150

250 / 125

250 / 100

45° splay kerbs

75 / 75
300 / 150

75 / 75
250 / 125

half batter kerbs

12½° to 15° typical

300 / 200 / 150

250 / 150 / 125

125 / 25 / 150

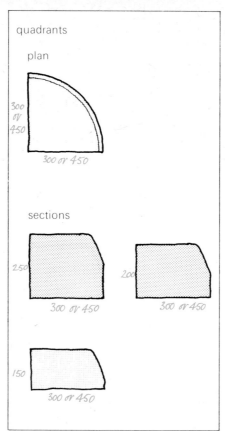

quadrants

plan

300 or 450

300 or 450

sections

250
300 or 450

200
300 or 450

150
300 or 450

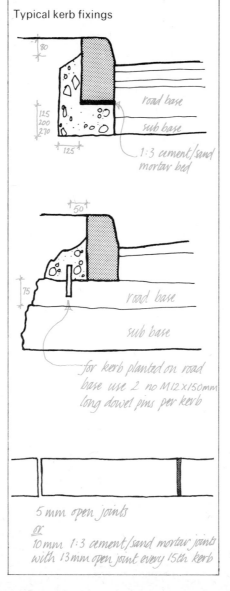

Typical kerb fixings

80

road base

sub base

125
200
270

125

1:3 cement/sand mortar bed

50

75

road base

sub base

for kerb planted on road base use 2 no M12 × 150mm long dowel pins per kerb

5 mm open joints

or

10 mm 1:3 cement/sand mortar joints with 13 mm open joint every 15th kerb

Pre-cast concrete kerbs and quadrants are not as durable as granite and as they become damaged or worn they should be replaced.

Comparative laid costs
Grey precast concrete kerb
Secondhand granite kerb – expensive
New granite kerb – very expensive

Recommendations
If new or second hand granite cannot be used, in urban areas use half batter kerbs.

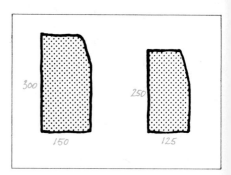

300 / 150

250 / 125

In light traffic and semi-rural areas use 45° splay or continental kerbs.

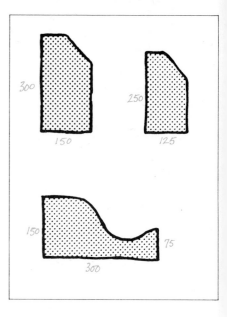

300 / 150

250 / 125

150 / 300 / 75

Useful names (for addresses see chapter 21)
Atlas Stone Co Ltd
Charcon Products Ltd
Concrete (Northern Ireland) Ltd
Mono Concrete Ltd

6.3 Crossovers/ ramped kerbs

Wherever there is heavy traffic across a kerb – pedestrians or vehicles – a

crossover should be provided. This involves lowering the kerb from its typical 100mm to 25mm thus allowing wheelchairs, prams and motor vehicles a relatively easy passage.

All other crossover details are as for kerb details 6.1 and 6.2.

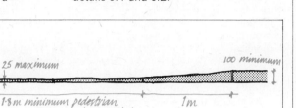

6.4 Edgings/ mowing strips

Edgings are merely kerbs of small dimension.

They are used as light duty kerbs, to define the boundaries between footpaths, grassed areas, paved areas etc.

Edgings should not be used as the risers for steps with rubble or concrete infill treads, if subsidence or compaction occurs the steps become exceedingly dangerous.

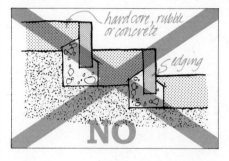

Edgings can be used to retain water by leaving them proud of the surrounding surfaces.

Where edgings border grassed areas they should be laid 25mm below the level of the grass, and where the grass abuts a vertical surface, the edging is laid on the flat to form a mowing strip.

Materials and finishes
Generally grey pre-cast concrete, with ex-mould finish as standard. Colour may be introduced by using cement pigments or by exposing the aggregate, but any deviation from the standard will increase cost.

Timber used as edgings should be well treated with creosote before use. On cut ends, apply creosote liberally with a brush. Granite setts, non-absorbent and frost resistent bricks and clay paviors can also be used as edgings.

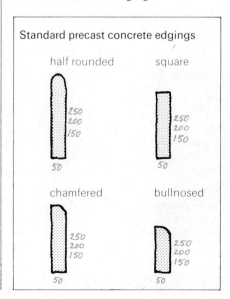

Useful names (as 6.2)

49

Vertical edgings

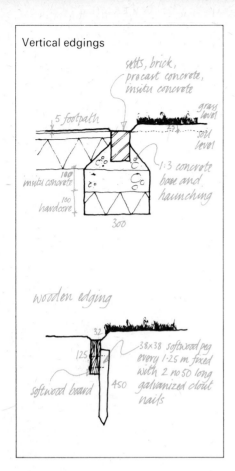

setts, brick, precast concrete, insitu concrete

grass level

5 footpath

soil level

100 insitu concrete

1:3 concrete base and haunching

100 hardcore

300

wooden edging

32

125

38×38 softwood peg every 1·25 m fixed with 2 no 50 long galvanized clout nails

softwood board

450

Mowing strip
to be used where grass abuts buildings and raised obstructions

setts, brick, precast concrete, insitu concrete

5 fall

‡18 1:3 cement mortar bed and haunching

100 hardcore

50

200 mm

Splash strip
to be used where soil abuts buildings and raised obstructions

setts, brick, precast concrete, insitu concrete

5 fall

soil level

‡18 1:3 cement mortar bed and haunching

150 1:3 insitu concrete base

100 hardcore

200 mm

50

Not surprisingly maintenance costs relate inversely to the quality of the edging material:

Granite – Negligible

Pre-cast concrete and brick – not so

hard wearing, occasional replacement cost.

Timber – limited life, replacement cost.

Comparative costs
Timber
Precast concrete – expensive
Stock bricks – expensive
Clay paviors – expensive
Secondhand granite setts – very expensive

Recommendations
Though more difficult to lay than precast concrete, granite setts provide the best edging material, being virtually indestructible. Bricks are more colourful than granite or concrete, but have to be very carefully selected to avoid frost problems.

Concrete and timber are impossible to lay to tight curves, being only available in long lengths.

Timber has a limited life and incurs replacement costs.

Concrete is fairly easily chipped and cracked, and occasional replacements are needed.

Useful names (as 6.2)

6.5 Safety kerbs

Safety kerbs are used to physically separate potentially heavy traffic from pedestrians, road signs and lighting columns, or from other traffic. The kerbs should be designed to redirect the vehicle back along its proper path without any sudden halt or overturning.

The kerbs are made from high strength concrete, often containing granite aggregate, the minimum compressive strength is 55MNm² at 28 days.

The surface finish is smooth ex-mould and the weight is approximately 220 kg/914mm.

45° and 60° quadrants are available. Straight sections can be laid to radii of 7.0m or more, for radii less than that, special kerb lengths, having joints splayed on the radial line, must be used. The kerb must be laid to line, with the road edge nosing 25mm above road level.

Precast concrete safety kerb

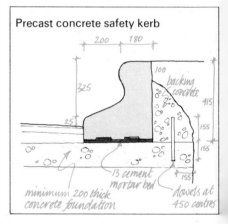

200   180

325

100 backing concrete

415

25

155

155

13 cement mortar bed

dowels at 450 centres

155

minimum 200 thick concrete foundation

Maintenance
This kerb is virtually maintenance free.

The cost is little different from any other traffic barrier: see 7.2.

Recommendations
Where there is a high risk of vehicles leaving the road and colliding with pedestrians or road side equipment, safety kerbs should be used. These are designed to retain the vehicles on the road.

It should be noted that these kerbs are not infallible, and at extreme speeds and angles of approach, vehicles have been known to leap over them.

Useful names (for addresses see chapter 21)
Redland Precast Ltd (Ellis – Trieff)

6.6 Refuges/ islands

Traffic islands and refuges are exactly what their names imply: raised areas in the middle of roads.

They are used to protect objects sited in the middle of the road: bollards, lighting columns, traffic lights and signs.

On busy roads, they are welcomed by pedestrians who can, for example, negotiate their crossing in two separate stages across two way traffic.

Islands and refuges can be temporary or permanent.

Temporary islands and refuges are usually made from timber, steel or concrete and are placed, ragbolted or stuck onto the existing surface.

Permanent islands should preferably be made from natural stone or steel – being most resistant to vehicle attack – and fixed into the road surface with suitable backing.

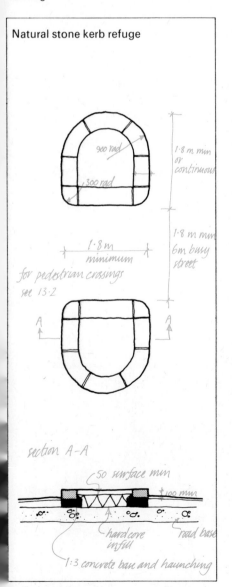

Natural stone kerb refuge

section A-A

Sectional steel refuge
galvanized steel sections bolted together

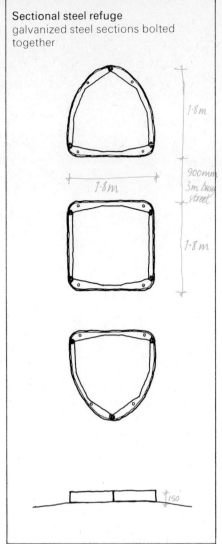

These are fixed onto the road surface with M18 x 150 ragbolts, then filled with 100mm concrete or rubble and 50mm hard surfacing.

Siting
By their very nature, islands and refuges are a barrier to vehicles, and great care must be taken in their siting. It is dangerous for them to project beyond the kerb line at junctions, where there should be at least 3m setback.

Granite and steel have negligible maintenance costs.
Pre-cast concrete can be damaged and replacements are necessary from time to time.
Timber is not very durable and should only be used for temporary islands.

Recommendations
For a permanent island or refuge, granite is the best material to use. For temporary islands pre-cast concrete or steel is better than timber.

At complicated traffic junctions where there are many small islands, which should not be walked on by pedestrians, the islands should be mounded with hard finishes (see 1.6.). Where mounds might obstruct motorists' sight lines, the maximum height should not exceed 0.8m. Mounded islands have the advantage of being self-cleaning, self-draining and maintenance free and they also obviate the need for guard rails.

Very large islands can be grassed over or planted with hardy ground-cover, shrubs and trees. Grassed areas need frequent maintenance, and access and off road parking must be provided for a motor-mower and its transporter.

In busy shopping streets carrying two way traffic, for example, Oxford Street, London, it can be very advantageous to pedestrians to provide a continuous refuge, at least 1.8m wide, along the centre of the road. In this case the road width should be 7.8m. Openings should be left for crossing and turning vehicles. At major pedestrian crossing points, crossovers should be provided (see 6.3) with 0.6m width allowed per person.

Where essential islands or refuges are frequently struck by vehicles, they should be painted gloss white as this makes them more visible, and thus more easily avoided.

Useful Names (for addresses see chapter 21)
Franco Traffic Signs Ltd
Hale & Hale Engineers Ltd

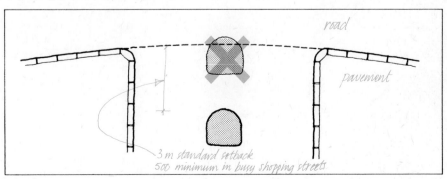

BARRIERS/GATES

Barriers/gates

All the items in this chapter are designed to separate one thing from another, or many things from many others, or any combination of these, mainly in the interests of safety.

Some barriers rely on their physical bulk and strength for their effect, at the other extreme, a slight visual and largely psychological effect may be all that is required.

Before deciding whether to specify any barriers for a particular site, first consider the functions of the site, then the necessity of a barrier. This is not so easy or straight forward, as it may appear at first sight, and often great conflicts arise, as to the degree of separation desired or required.

It is fairly obvious what might be needed to prevent pedestrians or vehicles from falling over steep drops, but it is far from obvious, whether, in a busy shopping street, one should erect barriers to prevent pedestrians from crossing the road at any point other than signalled crossings, or whether one should provide a continuous central refuge along the road and no barriers at all.

The argument inevitably hinges on the degree of individual liberty which can be allowed, before safety suffers too much. On the one hand there is regimentation, delay and frustration and on the other, absolute freedom for any pedestrian or vehicle to go wherever he will, with no regard for the safety of others.

For human beings to feel happy and satisfied with their surroundings, the balance must lean rather more towards freedom than confinement, and barriers should only be provided where absolutely necessary.

As a guide, if a situation exists where, due to crowd pressures, a hapless unfortunate might be propelled, beyond his or her own volition, into an area of danger; a good case can be made for the provision of physical barriers.

It must be borne in mind, that accident figures can rarely offer any sort of conclusive evidence one way or the other. The protagonists of opposing views often use the same figures to support diametrically opposing arguments.

In a cluttered environment, barriers should be as light and visually transparent as possible whilst still achieving the necessary separation.

Barriers which allow uninterrupted vision should be used at places where it is important not to obstruct sight lines.

Where the environment is less cluttered, barriers can be a strong design feature. The use of local natural materials, strong colours etc can provide special interest.

When access is required through a barrier, gates or rising barriers will have to be provided.

7.1 Pedestrian barriers/guard rails

Barriers separating pedestrians from vehicles are known by a variety of names: pedestrian guard rails, pedestrian steel parapets, pedestrian barriers, barrier railings, handrails, balustrading, pedestrian barrier rail, etc.

In this manual, these barriers will be called pedestrian guard rails.

They are used to separate pedestrians from moving motor vehicles at points of particular danger, such as, junctions, bends, brows of hills, and so on.

Many materials are used for guard rails: timber, aluminium, cast iron; with the vast majority being made from galvanised steel tubing.

Strict regulations govern the design of guard rails, which should conform to the relevant British Standards: see chapter 20.

The Greater London Council uses a standard design of pedestrian guard rail which has two types of panel, one for use where sight lines must not be obstructed, and the other for all the usual locations where guard rails are needed.

Guard rails are usually left in their natural finish or painted 'Worboys' grey. In positions where they are frequently knocked down, it will help visibility if they are painted gloss white and, if possible, illuminated by the light from an adjacent road light.

In areas of special environmental interest, guard rails may be painted in special colours, for example, gold in Parliament Square, London.

This type of guard rail requires careful measuring on site before manufacture. Some other types are self-raking on slopes up to 1 in 6 (16%) and so standard panels can be kept in reserve, for replacement purposes, which avoids any waiting for the manufacture of 'specials' for slopes.

Recommendations
The safest places for pedestrians to cross roads, other than subways or footbridges, are at zebra or pelican crossings: see 13.2. Not surprisingly, the area within 50m of these crossings is especially dangerous to pedestrians, and it is quite common to erect guard rails at these points to prevent pedestrians walking into the road. This is unfortunately necessary due to the fact the demarkated crossings are rarely wide enough or sited exactly on the pedestrians natural line of travel, and so the tendency is to cross near, rather than on, the crossing provided.

Unpainted guard rails seldom require any maintenance except when they are attacked by errant motor vehicles, and then, more often than not, they will have to be replaced.

If guard rails are painted, they will require repainting at regular intervals. These intervals vary from authority to authority, and can be anything from annually upwards.

Long lengths of guard rails give any environment an undue effect of severe confinement and regimentation.

When pedestrian and vehicle separation is desirable, thought should be given to possible alternatives rather than specifying guard rails as a matter of course. Continuous central refuges, small aqueducts, planters, bollards, trees, are all ways in which pedestrians can be screened from vehicles, and are infinitely preferable to the usual guard rails which seem to be springing up everywhere.

If there is absolutely no alternative, guard rails should be erected at points of particular danger to pedestrians.

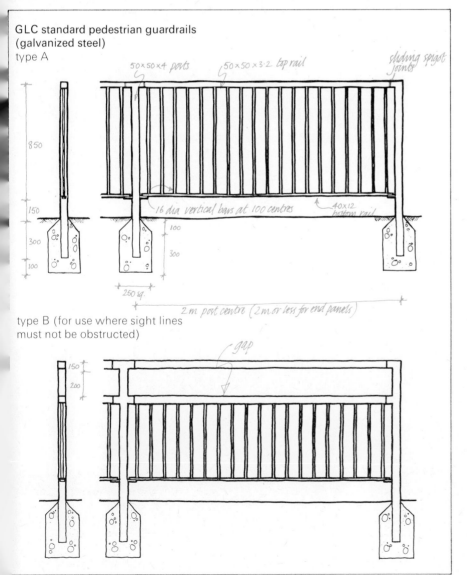

GLC standard pedestrian guardrails (galvanized steel)
type A

50×50×4 posts   50×50×3.2 top rail   sliding spigot joints

850

150

300

100

16 dia vertical bars at 100 centres   40×12 bottom rail

100

300

250 sq.

2 m post centre (2 m or less for end panels)

type B (for use where sight lines must not be obstructed)

gap

150
200

Useful names (for addresses see chapter 21)
Abacus Municipal Ltd
Bergo Ltd
British Aluminium Co Ltd
British Steel Corporation
Albert Cook & Son (Founders) Ltd
Furnitubes International Ltd
Glynwed Tubes & Structures Ltd
Hale & Hale Engineering Ltd
Non-Corrosive Metal Products Ltd
Norman & Sons (Marketing) Ltd
Starkey Gardner Ltd
Town & Country Steelcraft Ltd

7.2 Traffic barriers/safety fences

Traffic barriers and safety fences, are barriers, usually made of steel, aluminium or concrete, which physically prevent vehicles from leaving the road at points of special danger, such as sharp bends and steep drops or slopes, or crossing central reservations.

The barrier should redirect any errant vehicle back on to the road and parallel to the barrier, and the vehicle should not stop abruptly nor overturn after striking the barrier.

Barriers are of two types, either road-edge barriers, or median barriers, where the barrier is positioned on or as a central reservation separating two streams of traffic travelling in opposite directions.

The Road Research Laboratory has done exhaustive studies on traffic barriers and safety fences and has a vast array of knowledge on the subject.

In the urban environment traffic barriers are needed on urban motorways and primary distributors, where speeds are high, and at points of special danger on general purpose roads.

Traffic barriers should be erected on both sides of roads on embankments 6m high or more, and on the outer edge of roads where the radius is 850m or less and the embankment height 3m or more.

Barriers may also be needed: on an embankment where there is a road, railway or river at the foot, on bridges with lightly built parapets or to protect bridge piers or other obstructions on the central reserve or verges.

In urban areas, where space is often at a premium and median widths are

Typical traffic barriers
steel 'W' beam on knockdown post

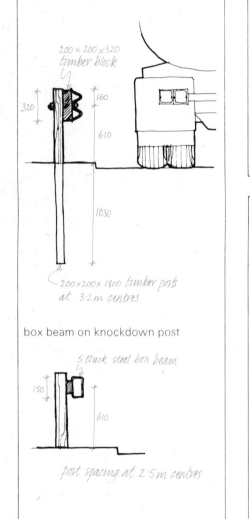

box beam on knockdown post

two box beams on knockdown post

Precast concrete barriers

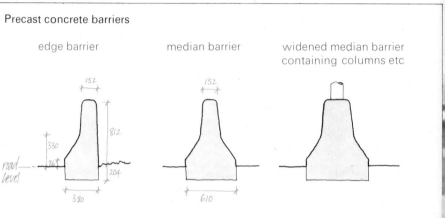

edge barrier   median barrier   widened median barrier containing columns etc

Spring steel buffer barriers

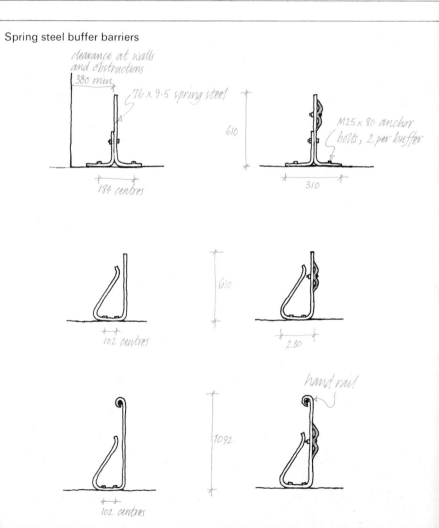

necessarily small, the continuous rigid concrete median barrier can be very effective in preventing cross-median accidents and can also be used to protect centrally mounted lighting columns etc.

Traffic barriers are normally left natural finish or painted 'Worboys' grey, and at points of special danger, it may be helpful to paint black and white bands or chevrons 1 m wide on the beams.

A particular type of barrier has been developed to protect walls and the like in car parks. It is made of spring steel and acts rather like a railway buffer. W beams may be added if required, for extra protection and strength.

7.3 Temporary cones/barriers/ lamps

Such things as road works, site works and broken paving all constitute temporary hazards. Whenever a temporary hazard occurs on a public road or footpath, or private property open to the public, it must be cordoned off by a row of traffic cones (on roads) or a temporary barrier. These should be illuminated, during the hours of darkness by road danger lamps showing a yellow light.

Barriers should be portable, stable and appear substantial, but not so substantial as to cause excessive damage if struck (DoE recommendation).

Nowadays, barriers can be divided into two basic types: either brightly coloured supports which can be linked by plastic boards; or brightly coloured plastic tape, chains or scarecrow pendants strung between iron bars hammered into the ground.

The bright colour, red or orange, can be made more intense by the addition of 'day-glo' fluorescent material, or by the addition of highly reflective particles of glass as in reflective road studs.

Traffic cones
rubber or flexible plastic

cones and planks

Expanding barrier
red painted steel

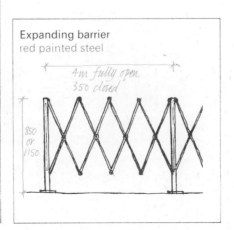

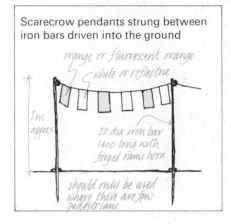
Scarecrow pendants strung between iron bars driven into the ground

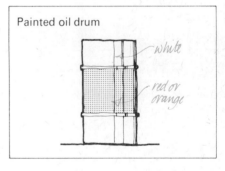
Painted oil drum

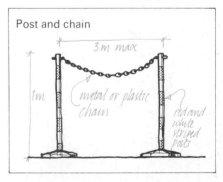
Post and chain

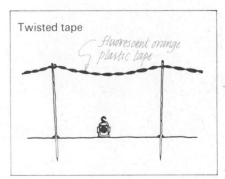
Twisted tape

Useful names (for addresses see chapter 21)
British Aluminium Co Ltd
British Steel Corporation
Brockhouse Berry Ltd
Durafencing Ltd
Glasdon Ltd
Road Research Ltd
Road Research Laboratory

To avoid confusion different types of barriers should not be used at the same time on any one site.

Road danger lamps
Road danger lamps must show a yellow light and be placed at regular intervals along the line of an obstruction or midway between traffic cones.

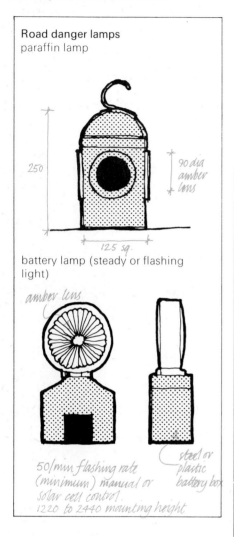

Road danger lamps
paraffin lamp

250
90 dia amber lens
125 sq.

battery lamp (steady or flashing light)

amber lens

steel or plastic battery box

50/min flashing rate (minimum) manual or solar cell control.
1220 to 2440 mounting height

7.4 Fences/ railings/walls/ screen walls/ retaining walls

Fences and walls, being usually assembled, from a number of relatively small components, have virtually unlimited scope for design.

The type of fence or wall selected, is largely governed by the degree of screening, security and strength required, and by cost. It cannot be stated too strongly however, that the appearance of a fence or wall has a great influence on its surroundings, even a small fence 2m high by 10m long covers the considerable area of 20m².

Fences and walls can vary between the extremely solid and massive and the very light and transparent.

The GLC has a standard range of walls and fences, which have been designed to suit most requirements economically, with low maintenance costs.

Where there is a vertical drop of 600mm or more a barrier of some sort should be provided.

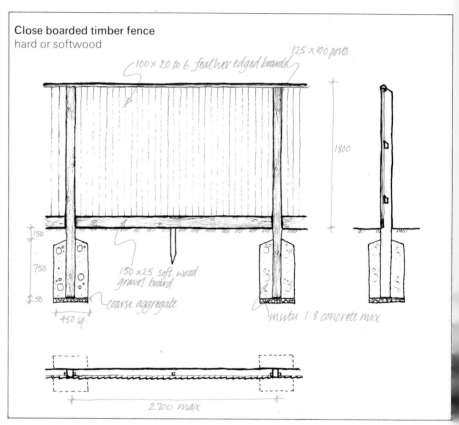

Close boarded timber fence
hard or softwood

125 x 100 posts
100 × 20 to 6 feather edged boards
1800
150
750
50
450 sq.
150 x 25 soft wood gravel board
course aggregate
insitu 1:8 concrete mix
2700 max

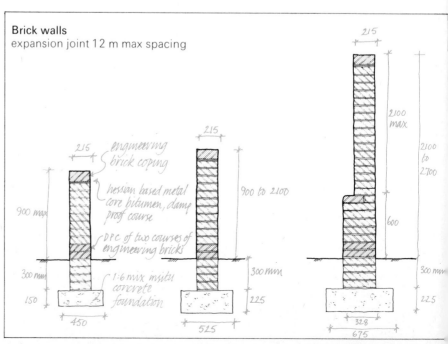

Brick walls
expansion joint 12 m max spacing

215
2100 max
2100 to 2700
215
engineering brick coping
900 to 2100
600
hessian based metal core bitumen, damp proof course
900 max
DPC of two courses of engineering bricks
300 mm
300 mm
300 mm
1:6 mix insitu concrete foundation
150
225
225
450
525
328
675

58

Bow topped mild steel fence
painted on hot dip galvanized finish

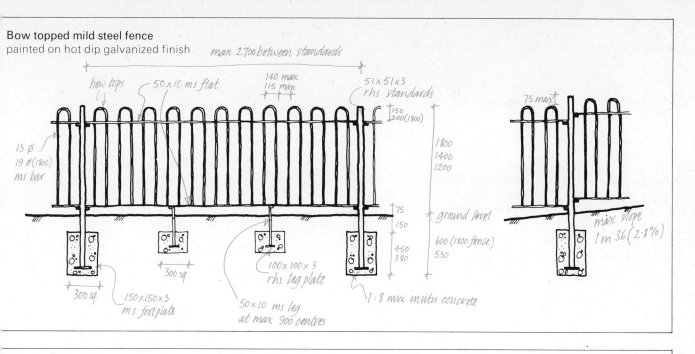

Chain link fence
galvanized or plastic coated

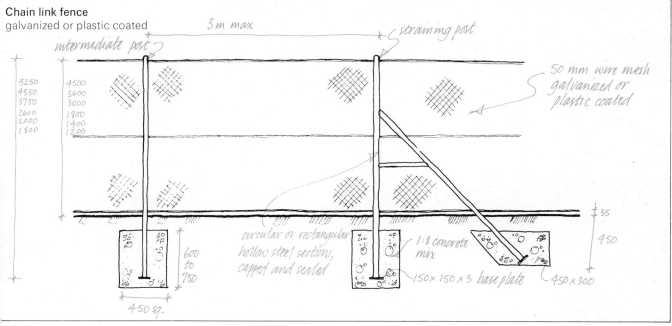

Drystone wall
local materials should be used if at all possible

For open spaces, parks etc a more rural type of fence or wall is preferred. Wherever possible, local materials should be used; dry-stone walling, timber in wooded areas etc.

Screen walls
Screen walls are a way of providing privacy without giving the impression of excessive enclosure. They are generally constructed from precast concrete blocks, having an open pattern, in exactly the same way as normal concrete building block walls. The open pattern provides a screen but allows light and air to penetrate.

Screen walling makes an ideal support for climbing plants and creepers etc.

Retaining walls
Retaining walls are used at abrupt

Mortised timber fence
hard or softwood

Lincolnshire timber fence

Mild steel fence

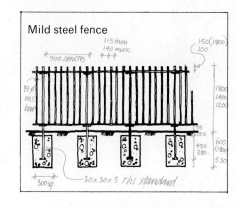

changes of level, to hold back materials such as earth and rubble which are in themselves unstable and which otherwise might assume their normal angle of response: see 1.7.

They may be constructed from normal building material, brick, in situ concrete, or nowadays, more conveniently, from pre-cast concrete solid or interlocking crib wall units.

Less severe slopes can be stabilised by the use of plastic or metal mesh staked in place, or concrete and grass slabs: see 4.5.

Typical screen walling
precast concrete units

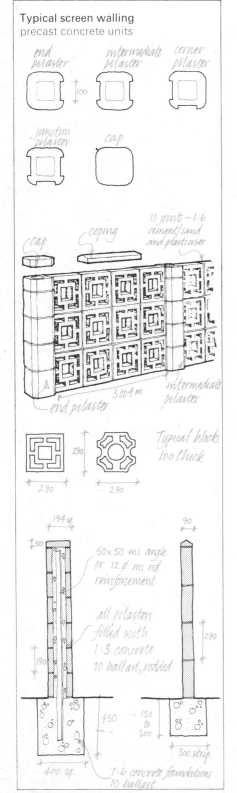

end pilaster

intermediate pilaster

corner pilaster

junction pilaster

cap

100

cap

coping

10 joints – 1:6 cement/sand and plasticiser

end pilaster

3 to 4 m

intermediate pilaster

Typical blocks 100 thick

290

290

290

194 sq

90

50

50 × 50 ms angle or 12 ø ms rod reinforcement

all pilasters filled with 1:3 concrete 10 ballast, rodded

290

190

450

150 to 300

300 strip

400 sq

1:6 concrete foundations 10 ballast

Typical retaining walls
brick retaining wall

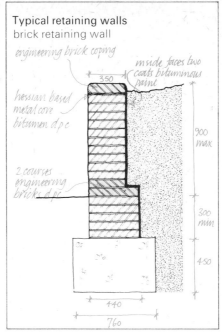

engineering brick coping

350

inside faces two coats bituminous paint

hessian based metal core bitumen d.p.c

900 max

2 courses engineering bricks d.p.c

300 min

450

440

760

Precast concrete units

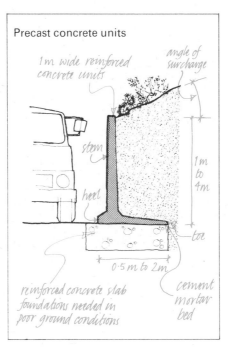

1 m wide reinforced concrete units

angle of surcharge

stem

heel

1 m to 4 m

toe

0·5 m to 2 m

cement mortar bed

reinforced concrete slab foundations needed in poor ground conditions

Precast concrete crib wall

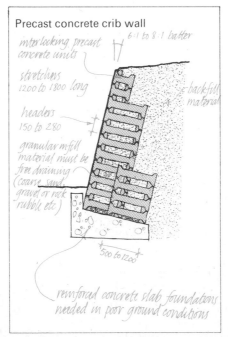

interlocking precast concrete units

6:1 to 8:1 batter

stretchers 1200 to 1800 long

backfill material

headers 150 to 280

granular infill material must be free draining (coarse sand gravel or rock rubble etc)

500 to 1200

reinforced concrete slab foundations needed in poor ground conditions

Staked mesh

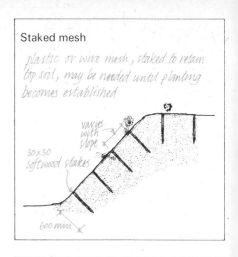

plastic or wire mesh, staked to retain top soil, may be needed until planting becomes established

varies with slope

30 × 30 softwood stakes

600 min

Concrete/grass slabs

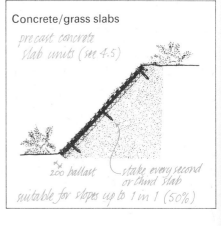

precast concrete slab units (see 4.5)

200 ballast

stake every second or third slab

suitable for slopes up to 1 in 1 (50%)

Useful names (for addresses see chapter 21)
Abacus Municipal Ltd
ARC Concrete Ltd
Atlas Stone Co Ltd
Brooklyns Westbrick Ltd
Buffalo Fence Ltd
Colorguard Ltd
Durafencing Ltd
Greater London Council
KUFA Plastics Ltd
Marley Buildings Ltd
Marshalls & Sons Ltd
Mono Concrete Ltd
Non-Corrosive Metal Products Ltd
PJP Trading Ltd
Redland Precast Ltd
Reinforced Concrete Construction Co Lt
Townscape Products Ltd
UAC International Ltd

7.5 Gates/rising barriers

Gates and rising barriers are used to control access through barriers.

Gates normally open and close by swivelling horizontally, and rising barriers, as the name implies, open and close by swivelling vertically.

Gates can be used to add interest to their surroundings, for example, the cast iron gates to Kensington Gardens, London. They are often extremely distinctive and arresting features in an area.

Manufacturers frequently use the gates to their offices, works and factories as an extension of their promotional activities, largely to very good effect. This practise should be encouraged at all times, the odd 'gem' is sure to turn up now and then.

5 bar timber gate
hard or softwood

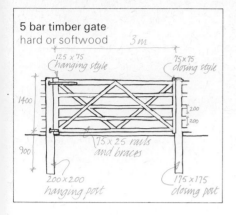

Bow topped mild steel gate
paint on hot dip galvanized finish

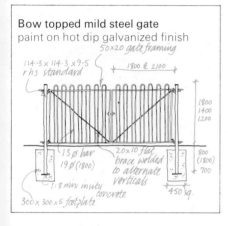

Gates for chain link fence

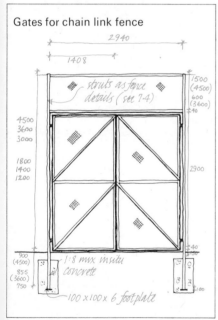

Close boarded timber gate
hard or softwood

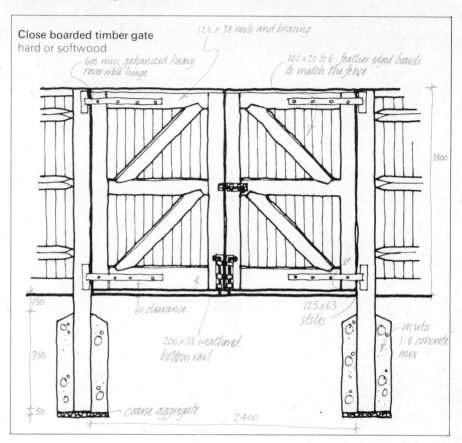

Gallows gate
painted galvanized finish

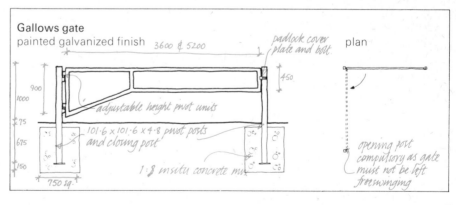

Hinged barrier
barriers may be manual or power controlled

manually operated barrier

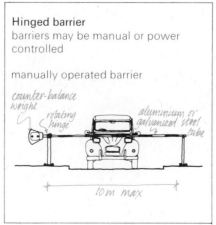

Rising step barrier
electrically powered

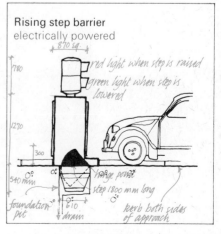

Useful names (for addresses see chapter 21)
APT Ltd
Brady & Co Ltd
Godwin Warren Engineering Ltd
Tully Engineering Co Ltd
JAC International Ltd

BOLLARDS

8.1 Illuminated traffic bollards

Definition and uses

A traffic bollard is a device placed on a refuge or traffic island to warn drivers of those obstructions. It may indicate by means of a prescribed traffic sign the direction to be taken by vehicles. The signs are either of two sizes 270mm diameter or 600mm diameter.

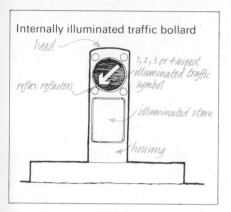

Internally illuminated traffic bollard

head
1, 2, 3 or 4 aspect illuminated traffic symbol
reflex reflectors
illuminated stem
housing

Materials and finishes

Bollards are usually made from sheet steel, plastics or cast alloy which should have at least 2 years satisfactory outdoor performance, that is if they can survive for so long without being knocked down.

They are lit by hot cathode fluorescent lamps with at least two separately fused circuits.

Construction and fixing

Fixing is by holding down bolts into foundation concrete. The latest trend is for frangible types, which have a fixed base, with the housing connected by shear bolts, and a snatch plug to disconnect the electricity supply on 'knock down'.

Flexible plastic bollards generally sustain little or no damage on 'knock down' and can be refixed repeatedly.

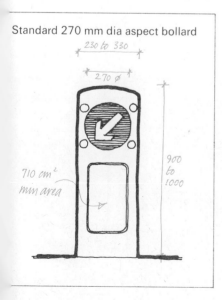

Standard 270 mm dia aspect bollard

230 to 330
270 ⌀
710 cm² mm area
900 to 1000

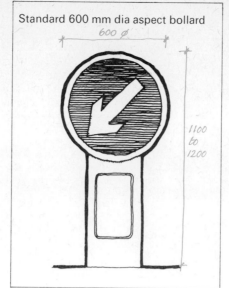

Standard 600 mm dia aspect bollard

600 ⌀
1100 to 1200

Siting

On a refuge or traffic island bollards are normally sited on the centre line 450mm from the nose of the refuge.

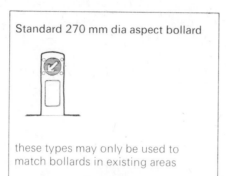

Standard 270 mm dia aspect bollard

these types may only be used to match bollards in existing areas

these squashable or hinging plastic bollards should only be used at sites where bollards are frequently knocked down

spring hinge

Standard 600 mm dia aspect bollard

this type should not be used

Maintenance

Not surprisingly, traffic bollards are frequently knocked down. At especially tempting sites, in order to minimize maintenance costs, a squashable plastic bollard is preferred to a traditional metal and plastic one.

Comparative costs

Flexible Plastic
Traditional
Frangible traditional

Recommendations

Bollards should be as simple as possible both visually and geometrically.

Flexible plastic bollards need little maintenance. They are self-coloured, so they are not disfigured by scratches, and minor dents spring out again.

A frangible base fixing minimizes damage and danger.

In places where 'knock down' is infrequent or never happens, traditional steel bollards are ideal. They have a long life, are easy to service, and tend to be much more simple in design than any plastic bollards yet available.

Useful names (for addresses see chapter 21)
Bergo Limited
Claudgen Traffic Signs
Franco Limited
Haldo Developments
Hale and Hale Engineering Limited
Hills (Patents) Limited
Lindvale Plastics Limited
Pearce-Gowshall Limited
Road Signs – Franco Limited
Staines Tinware Manufacturing Co Ltd
Trevor Morrison Engineering Limited
Truesigns Limited
Undivale Plastics Limited

8.2 Barrier bollards

Definitions and uses

Bollards used as barriers can be subdivided into two main groups; those which physically deter a vehicle and those which visually deter a vehicle. Both types allow free pedestrian and two-wheeled penetration.

Trees are successful as both physical and visual bollards and their use should be considered more often.

Materials and finishes

The physical deterrent types are generally large and heavy, being made from cast iron, steel, concrete and other high mass materials, solidly bedded into mass concrete foundations.

The visual deterrent types are generally thin and light in weight, being made from plastics, timber, light gauge metal tubing etc. The latest types are made from flexible plastics which allow the bollards to regain their normal shape should they be run over or squashed.

Standard concrete bollards

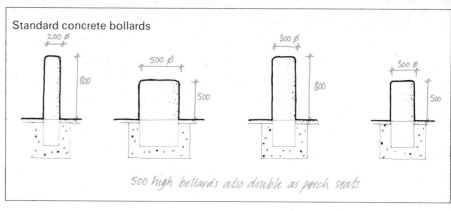

500 high bollards also double as perch seats

Visual deterrents

used mainly to delineate the edges of roads, parking bays, driveways and so on

vehicles generally suffer relatively minor damage on impact

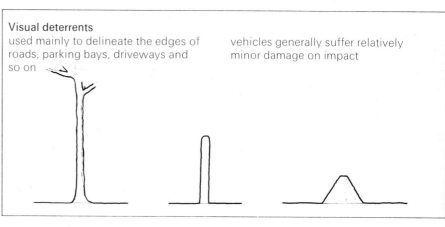

Physical deterrents

large size and heavy weight will stop majority of vehicles
bollards should be reinforced (to prevent rolling after impact) when sited near busy pedestrian areas

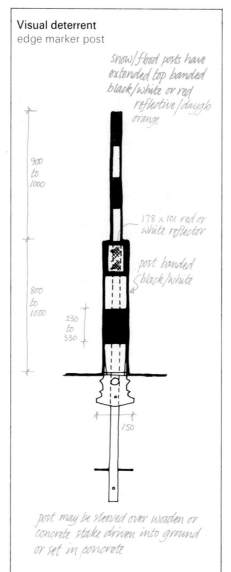

Visual deterrent
edge marker post

snow/flood posts have extended top banded black/white or red reflective/dayglo orange

900 to 1000

178 x 101 red or white reflector

post banded black/white

800 to 1000

230 to 330

150

post may be sleeved over wooden or concrete stake driven into ground or set in concrete

Visual deterrent
flexible plastic edge marker post

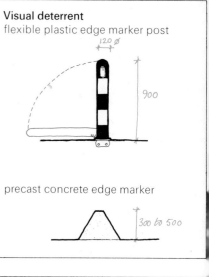

120 ø

900

precast concrete edge marker

300 to 500

Visual deterrent
historic cast iron bollard

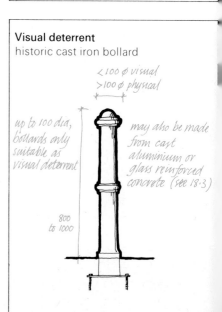

<100 ø visual
>100 ø physical

up to 100 dia, bollards only suitable as visual deterrent

may also be made from cast aluminium or glass reinforced concrete (see 18·3)

800 to 1000

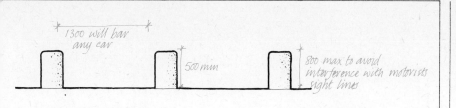

1300 will bar any car

500 mm

800 max to avoid interference with motorists sight lines

Metal and wooden bollards are invariably paint finished. Concrete is either mould or aggregate finished. Plastic is self coloured mould finish.

Trees make very good bollards!

Barrier bollards are almost always set into mass concrete foundations – but in soft ground, the light-weight plastic types can be sleeved onto timber or concrete stakes.

Siting
Barrier bollards are sited wherever vehicles have to be separated from something else, be it homo-sapiens, buildings or just empty space!

Traffic can be controlled by the size of bollards and the spacing between them.

Maintenance
Metal and timber require occasional maintenance. Concrete and plastic are virtually maintenance free.

Recommendations
Wherever possible trees should be used instead of bollards. They should initially be protected with sturdy stakes on the traffic approach side of the tree. They begin life as visual deterrents but quickly become physical deterrents and are relatively maintenance free.

Manufactured bollards should have geometrically simple shapes. They present much less clutter to the urban environment if they have no pronounced tapers or facets, unless designed specially for an historic site: see 18.3 'reproduction' furniture.

If pedestrians are likely to be in close contact, bollards should be smooth finished with no sharp edges.

Low, large diameter bollards 500mm high can also be used as seats.

Useful names (for addresses see chapter 21)
Adaptaform Plastics Limited
Atlas Stone Co Limited
Berger Traffic Markings Limited
Bergo Limited
Franco Traffic Signs Limited
Glasdon Limited
Greater London Council
John Orme Limited
Marshalls & Son Limited
Mather & Smith Limited
Mono-Concrete Limited
Redland Precast Limited
Road Signs – Franco Limited
Townscape Products Limited
Nature – Trees

8.3 Locking bollards

Locking bollards are used to exclude vehicle access except by key holders: fire brigade and police etc.

More frequently they are used to prevent access to private parking spaces.

They either hinge down or can be physically removed from their sockets.

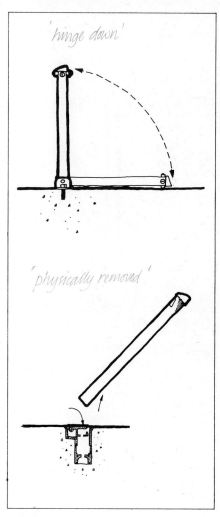

'hinge down'

'physically removed'

Materials and finishes
Locking bollards are usually constructed from hot dip galvanized steel, left in the natural finish.

Construction and fixing
Hinging bollards are bolted into mass concrete.

Removable bollards are housed in sockets, set into mass concrete.

Siting
If used in a continuous line, the bollards should be spaced at 1.2m centres.

When used for parking spaces they should alternate with fixed bollards, or trees, situated on the parking lines. For parking layouts see 4.3.

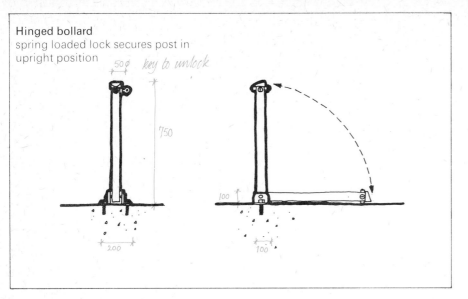

Hinged bollard
spring loaded lock secures post in upright position

50ø
key to unlock
750
100
200
100

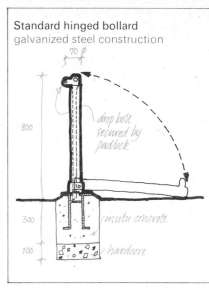

Standard hinged bollard
galvanized steel construction

70ø
drop bolt secured by padlock
800
300
insitu concrete
100
hardcore

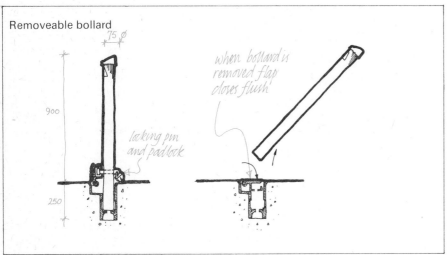

Removeable bollard

75ø
when bollard is removed flap closes flush
900
locking pin and padlock
250

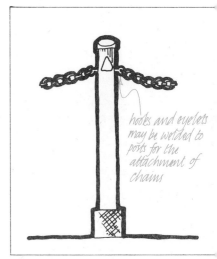

hooks and eyelets may be welded to posts for the attachment of chains

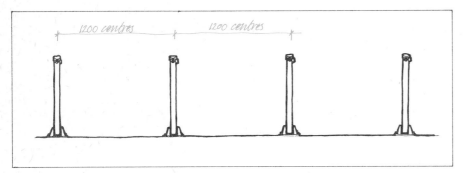

1200 centres
1200 centres

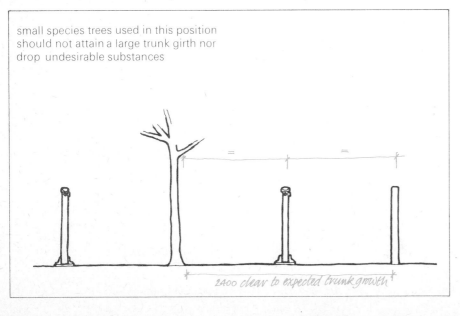

small species trees used in this position should not attain a large trunk girth nor drop undesirable substances

2400 clear to expected trunk growth

Maintenance
Locks, hinges and sockets require occasional oiling and leaves and dirt need to be cleaned from mechanisms and sockets.

Recommendations
There is little to choose between these two types of bollards.

The hinged down type is more convenient in use, but is mechanically complicated and less resistant to vandalism.

The removable bollard can be removed and mislaid!

Fixed bollards should match any accompanying locking bollards – they are usually manufactured in matching sets.

Useful names (for addresses see chapter 21)
Borer Engineering Ltd
EVB Engineering Limited (GLC)
George Fischer Sales Limited
Mather & Smith Ltd

8.4 Amenity lighting bollards

Amenity lighting bollards are used as physical and visual deterrents for vehicles. They also provide low level amenity lighting.

These are made from metal or reinforced concrete.

Metal is either non-ferrous or galvanised steel, which can be left in its natural finish or painted or plastic coated.

Concrete can be ex-mould or exposed aggregate finish.

The electrical lamps are usually protected by a polycarbonate diffuser.

Siting
The spacing of amenity lighting bollards is calculated from the performance-details available with each type. It is advisable to consult a lighting design engineer for the siting of these bollards.

Maintenance
The electrical components constitute the major maintenance cost. This is due largely to the high level of vandalism associated with lighting fittings of all types.

Recommendations
In areas where there is a high incidence of vandalism it is useless to install any lighting fittings which are not designed to overcome this threat, particularly illuminated bollards which are particularly enticing to vandals.

A vandalised bollard can be lethal to children if live electrical apparatus can be reached. Even when the bollard is so strong that it is almost unbreakable, a simple allen-headed screw is not an adequate fixing device to prevent unauthorised access. Fixings should be used which need a special key to open them. It is rare for a maintenance engineer to leave behind his special key more than once.

Care must be taken to site amenity lighting bollards so that the illumination is adequate and where needed, but not glaring into the eyes of passing motorists.

Useful names (for addresses see chapter 21)
Abacus Municipal Limited
C M Churchouse Limited
Concrete Utilities Limited
Frederick Thomas & Co Limited
Lumitron Limited
Mono Concrete Limited
Staines Tinware Manufacturing Co Limited
Trevor Morrison Engineering Ltd

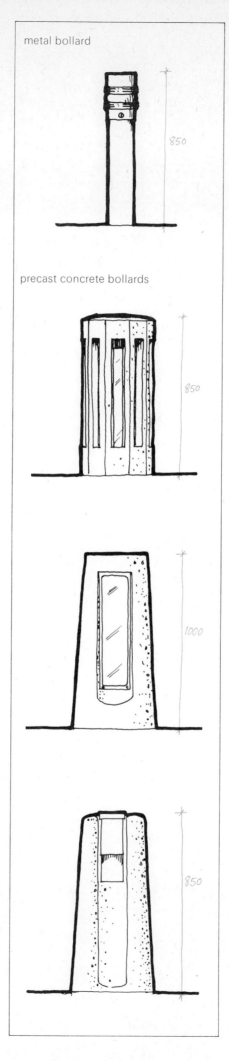

metal bollard

precast concrete bollards

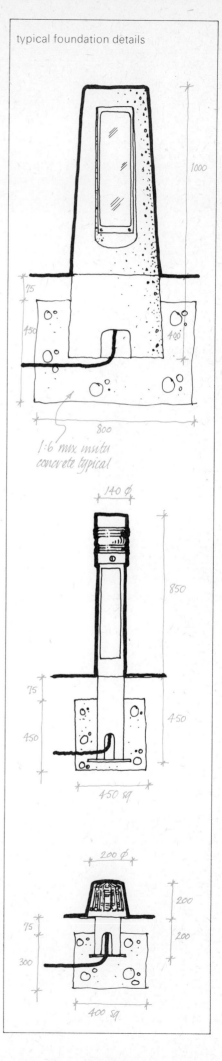

typical foundation details

1:6 mix insitu concrete typical

SUBWAYS/ UNDERPASSES

County Hall | Westminster Bridge - downstream

Subways/ underpasses

Subways and Underpasses are short tunnels which allow traffic uninterrupted movement under obstructions. Where the exit cannot be seen from the entrance, subways and underpasses are described as tunnels.

Subways are used by pedestrians and cyclists

Underpasses are used by motor vehicles and cyclists, though occasionally a footpath is provided alongside the road for the use of pedestrians.

Unless the underpass is very well ventilated, pollution levels can build up to alarming proportions (see 4.1), and so it is not generally advisable, in tunnels, to allow pedestrians and cyclists to share the same airspace as motor vehicles.

Each subway or tunnel has to be designed for its own particular location by specialist engineers, but guidance is given for minimum sizes etc so that the designer is aware of the general problems should he be contemplating using subways or underpasses.

9.1 Pedestrian subways

Definitions and uses

A pedestrian subway or tunnel allows pedestrians free passage under busy roads, road junctions, buildings, etc. In cities which have an underground railway network, subways are often combined with station entrances and underground booking halls.

Pedestrian subways can be entered by steps, ramps or both steps and ramps. Where space permits both ramps and steps should be provided at each entrance and exit. The slope of the ramps should not exceed 1:12 (8.3%). Handrails should be provided for both steps and ramps.

A subway for cyclists is like a pedestrian subway, with the exception that steps are not required and ramps are provided at each entrance and exit. The slope of the ramps should not exceed 1:20 (5%).

Materials and finishes

The traditional facing material of glazed ceramic tiles, besides being very clinical, has proved to be costly in terms of maintenance and replacement, always assuming that matching tiles are still available. Though spray paint can readily be removed from the tiles, the grout between the tiles is impossible to clean.

Recently the trend has been towards using natural concrete finishes, exposed aggregate, rough board shuttering, bush-hammered finish etc. Before the advent of the aerosol spray can, these finishes had some deterrent value against point source graffiti, but spray paint is virtually impossible to remove completely from any rough surface.

Rough surfaces soil quicker than smooth surfaces and are more difficult to clean, though of course they can always be painted.

Material which can be ignited by the flame from a cigarette lighter should not be used.

The most practical finish for subways is smooth concrete, coated with a special

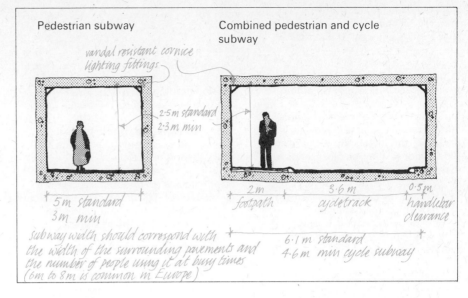

Pedestrian subway

Combined pedestrian and cycle subway

vandal resistant cornice lighting fittings

2·5 m standard
2·3 m min

5 m standard
3 m min

2 m footpath

3·6 m cycletrack

0·5 m handlebar clearance

subway width should correspond with the width of the surrounding pavements and the number of people using it at busy times (6m to 8m is common in Europe)

6·1 m standard
4·6 m min cycle subway

varnish or a paint system, which can be cleaned and maintained easily and periodically recoated.

For subway lighting see 11.2.

Construction

Subways are constructed from pre-cast concrete subway units or concrete cast in situ.

Sloping walls along the approach ramps or steps are much less claustrophobic than vertical walls.

The 'black hole' syndrome should be avoided at all cost.

In cycle subways a kerb should be provided 0.5m away from walls to allow clearance for handlebars, knuckles and knees!

As, regrettably, cyclists frequently use pedestrian subways, it is safer if a standard headroom height of 2.5m is specified for both pedestrian and cycle subways.

Any surface water collecting in a subway may have to be pumped up to the main drain level, if this is higher.

Siting

For subways to be successful and well used, they must be sited along main pedestrian and cycle routes, with easy open approaches and with the exit visible from the entrance.

If it is possible to site the subway and

the ramps or steps in a straight line, so that there are no recesses and corners where people may lurk, so much the better. If not, mirrors should be installed at blind corners, but these are a poor substitute for good layout and a prime target for vandals. The sight lines at corners should be 4m minimum.

Maintenance

In order to keep maintenance costs to a minimum, subway finishes should be simple and robust and all fittings must be vandal resistant.

Provision should be made for mains electricity and water points, for use by maintenance personnel.

All service points requiring occasional access should be contained in recessed compartments having very secure and robust flush doors opening into the subway.

As subways are often much lower than their immediate surroundings, they become a natural receptacle for wind-blown dirt, litter and rain. It is important that the cleaning of subways is very regular and to a high standard.

Comparative costs

Subways are more expensive, in terms of space and cost, than footbridges but are preferred by the majority of users, especially if they are properly laid out, supervised, lit and cleaned. They involve about half the rise and fall of footbridges with consequent savings in pedestrian time and difficulty of use.

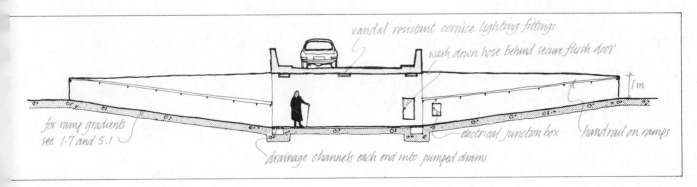

vandal resistant cornice lighting fittings

wash down hose behind secure flush door

1m

for ramp gradients see 1.7 and 5.1

electrical junction box

hand rail on ramps

drainage channels each end into pumped drains

Generally, the higher a subway is in the ground, the cheaper it will be in terms of space usage and cost of installation.

Recommendations
Subways should be as light and airy as possible: see 11.2 Subway lighting.

Light and bright colours and simple murals can help to make subways more attractive and interesting. Choose semi-gloss paint systems as gloss tends to make subways seem hostile and clinical.

The simpler the design of the subway and its fittings, the easier and cheaper will be the maintenance. Keeping subways spotlessly clean helps to reduce vandalism.

Internally illuminated signs or advertisement panels should not be used in subways. They are unnecessary targets for vandals (general subway lighting should be good enough to light non-illuminated signs and boards) and When broken can become lethal electrical hazards.

9.2 Underpasses

Definitions and uses
Underpasses are very similar to subways except that they are much larger, being designed for motor traffic, rather than pedestrians or cyclists.

Long underpasses, where the exit cannot be seen from the entrance are described as tunnels.

Underpasses go under obstructions at ground level. The entrance is reached by a downward sloping road, and after leaving the exit, the road slopes upwards, back to ground level. These are normally one way clearways. It is not surprising therefore that speeds in underpasses tend to be rather higher than speeds at the adjoining ground level roads. As a general rule avoid bends, straight underpasses lessen the risk of accidents caused by speeding vehicles.

Materials and finishes
The materials and finishes used in underpasses are largely the same as those used in subways. Where an underpass is not entered by pedestrians or cyclists, vandalism is not likely to be a problem, the main attack will come from vibration, exhaust emissions and vehicles bouncing off the walls.

In some underpasses, and particularly in tunnels, a separate lining of sheet plastic, aluminium etc is used, which is much easier and cheaper to maintain or replace than the structural walls themselves.

Underpasses should be painted in light colours, which helps driver visibility and minimises lighting requirements. For the lighting of underpasses see 11.5 Road lighting.

Construction and sizes
Underpasses are costly to build and take up a great deal of space, especially if busy roads run over them and slip roads are required to connect one to another. Nevertheless, underpasses can considerably improve conditions in many traffic congested areas, and are infinitely preferable, on environmental

grounds, to elevated flyovers.

The width of the underpass is dependant on the number of traffic lanes which need to run in each direction, and should conform to the normal design standards for roads.

Maximum gradient of approach ramps is 1 in 25 (4%).

Any surface water collecting in an underpass may have to be pumped up to the main drain level, it this is higher.

Siting
Underpasses are sited where it is advantageous for a road to avoid interference from other roads, railways or buildings etc.

Maintenance
In order to keep maintenance costs to a minimum, the fittings and finishes in an underpass should be as simple and robust as possible.

Provision should be made for mains electricity and water take off points for the use of maintenance personnel.

Recommendations
In urban areas, problems of conflicting traffic can often be solved by the construction of underpasses. These also allow the passage of traffic under areas where the construction of surface roads may be impossible, for example historic and conservation areas.

Underpasses should be as straight as possible, to minimize the risk of accidents.

The finishes chosen should be smooth and easy to clean and maintain.

Where space permits, the ramp wall should be sloped and preferably planted with hardy shrubs and trees.

Where the ramp walls must be vertical, coloured concrete can provide interest and points of reference.

The lighting in underpasses should be very carefully considered, see 11.7 Road lighting.

Minimum clearance requirements for speeds up to 80 km/h

1m 1·5 m preferred   varies   1m 1·5m pref   varies   1m 1·5m pref   varies   1m 1·5m pref

FOOTBRIDGES

10 Footbridges

Footbridges allow pedestrians uninterrupted passage over obstructions, busy roads, railways, rivers, buildings and so on.

They are designed by specialist structural engineers, and to rigid specifications. Manufacturers of footbridges generally have their own style of bridge which is quite dissimilar from that of their competitors and so the environmental designer has available a large selection of bridges, from which to choose the one most suitable for his requirements.

Footbridges have some advantages over pedestrian subways. Most importantly, they cost much less and can be erected very quickly, often in only one or two days on prepared foundations

However, footbridges crossing over busy roads suffer disadvantages which may be impossible to overcome at particular sites.

The minimum clearance of 5.1m above the road surface, means that the pedestrian diversion from the horizontal route, is more than twice that for subways. Consequently, ramps and steps have to be more than twice as long, which does not help those in most need, namely the disabled or elderly and people with prams and small children.

Where a footbridge is near buildings, there is often some degree of overlooking and a loss of privacy in the area surrounding the footbridge.

The effects of wind and weather are usually more severely felt on footbridges than at the surrounding ground level.

A footbridge is a large-scale item in any environment. In many places it can be used as a design feature but in certain areas, particularly conservation areas and those of special historic or architectural value, the visual intrusion would more than outweigh any benefits gained by pedestrians, and an alternative form of crossing should be provided.

The order of preference for road crossing by pedestrians is:

Surface crossings (pelican, zebra etc)
Subways
Footbridges

Footbridges and subways are best reserved for special cases, where the cost can be absorbed in large building and road works or in major redevelopment budgets.

Guardrails should be provided on either side of the approaches to a footbridge to encourage pedestrians to use the bridge rather than dodge the road traffic.

Footbridge with steps and ramps

front elevation

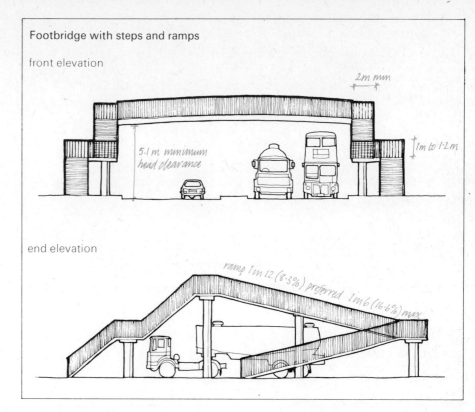

5.1 m minimum head clearance

2m min

1m to 1.2 m

end elevation

ramp 1 in 12 (8.3%) preferred 1 in 6 (16.6%) max

Spiral ramp footbridge

front elevation

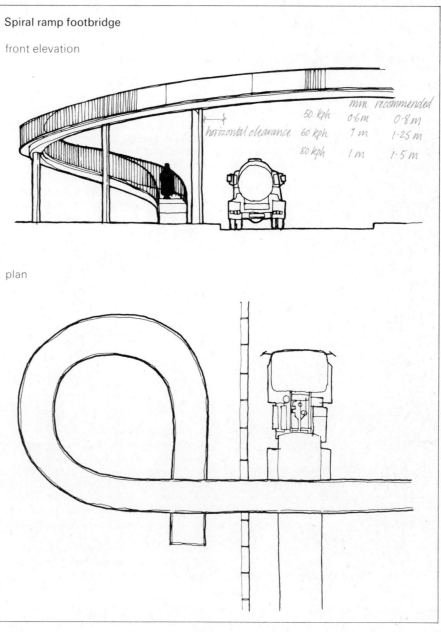

		min	recommended
	50 kph	0.6 m	0.8 m
horizontal clearance	60 kph	1 m	1.25 m
	80 kph	1 m	1.5 m

plan

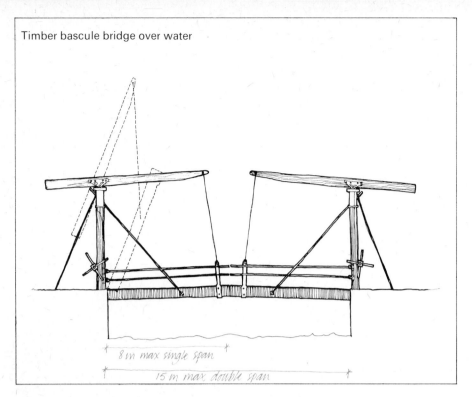

Timber bascule bridge over water

8 m max single span

15 m max double span

Generally, the best footbridges are simple and light in construction and appearance and economical in material and maintenance costs.

The majority of footbridges are largely constructed from structural steel or precast reinforced concrete, but lately, there has been a revival in structural timber bridges having single spans of up to 30m.

Steel should be galvanised or appropriately protected against corrosion.

Painted bridges lend themselves well to interesting colour schemes, which can do much to enliven, or blend with, the surrounding environment.

Though some timbers have a natural resistance to the effects of weather; Teak, Iroko, Keruing, etc, those which do not, should be treated with suitable preservatives which may be coloured if desired.

The decks of footbridges should be made from plain edged hardwood, such as Keruing, or from metal with an anti-skid finish. If the bridge has steep approach ramps, up to 1 in 6 gradient (16%) it is important to provide an anti-skid deck finish.

The handrails of footbridges should be smooth and free from splinters if wood, or rough welds if metal, or any protuberance which might cause injury, however slight.

Footbridges must have a minimum clear headroom of 5.1m where they cross a road, measured from the road to the underside of the bridge.

Pedestrian flow should not exceed 67 persons per minute per metre width, on the level to 1 in 20 (5%) gradient, or 47 persons per minute per metre width on steps or ramps steeper than 1 in 20 (5%) gradient. The minimum width should not be less than 2m.

Where possible, footbridges should have ramped approaches as well as steps.

Approach ramps should normally not be steeper than 1 in 12 (8.3%) though an absolute maximum slope of 1 in 6 (16.6%) may be necessary if space is severely restricted. In such locations it is usual to provide stepped ramps so that the going does not exceed 1 in 12 (8.3%): see 5.1.

Balustrades should be 1m to 1.2m high and they should be constructed so as to deter children from climbing through, or over, them.

Footbridges should drain in such a way that rainwater does not run onto vehicles or people, below.

Footbridges are normally erected on prepared reinforced concrete foundations.

Where bridges for pedestrians and perhaps light traffic, cross waterways, it can be less expensive to provide a simple timber lifting bridge, such as a bascule bridge, than to provide a fixed bridge with enough clearance for boats. In such cases the maximum single span is approximately 8m and dual span 15m.

Footbridges are required where large numbers of pedestrians need to cross busy roads, waterways, etc.

Crossing footbridges should not involve unnecessary climbing or long detours, if the bridge is to be well used. Where possible, bus stops should be sited close to footbridges.

Footbridges rarely require special lighting and tend to rely for their illumination on existing road lighting.

As the failure of any type of bridge could have serious consequences, it is essential that the inspection and maintenance of bridges is to a very high standard and regular frequency.

Footbridges are much less costly than subways and can be erected very quickly, with minimal disruption to pedestrians and road traffic.

Recommendations

Footbridges may be constructed where large numbers of pedestrians need to cross hazardous locations like busy roads or waterways.

They should be simple and light, both in construction and appearance and economical in maintenance costs.

Where space permits it is better if footbridges have continuous ramped approaches as well as steps.

Footbridges, painted with well designed colour schemes, can do much to enliven the surrounding environment. Or colour can also be used to integrate bridges with their surroundings.

Natural materials, such as timber and stone, can be used for the construction of small footbridges in parks and urban open spaces.

Useful names (for addresses see chapter 21)
Adamson Butterley Ltd
Anglian Building Products Ltd
British Steel Corporation *Tubes Division*
Burt Boulton (Timber) Ltd
Concrete Utilities (Bridges) Ltd
I G Engineering Co Ltd
Laird (Anglesey) Ltd
Sanders Tubecrafts Ltd
Sherbourne Engineering Ltd
South Coast Welders Ltd

Lighting

Exterior artificial lighting dates well back into history and has mainly been provided to increase the safety of people passing about their lawful business after dark. This is still the main purpose of exterior lighting installations today.

In towns the individual light carried by pedestrians is a thing of the past and everyone expects, as soon as they leave their front door, to find a well-lit path or roadway.

In pedestrian areas, sufficient light must be provided to establish confidence and it should be of a pleasing colour. Well-lit surroundings to dwellings, not only enhance the appearance of a residential area but also deter vandals and other undesirables.

Side streets are lit mainly for the benefit of pedestrians but lighting installations on traffic routes perform a dual function. They provide lighting not only to enable the pedestrian to walk about in safety but also to enable vehicular traffic to be driven safely and thereby reduce the number of pedestrian accidents which occur. Not surprisingly, during periods of enforced darkness or reduce lighting both the accident rate and crime rate have been found to increase.

Today with rising energy costs, the importance of good design in lighting cannot be over-emphasised.

The light sources need to be well placed and of the correct type, to enable a good job to be done with economy. Time and money spent in the design stage will earn dividends later.

11.1 Light sources and colours

Where running costs are of primary importance, the choice lies between economical monochromatic yellow light and 'white light', costing at least twice as much.

The monochromatic yellow is provided by low pressure sodium lighting, which is acceptable for traffic routes, but not good for pedestrian areas, because all plants and surfaces appear to be shades of brown and yellow.

'White light' is so called because colour discrimination is possible under this form of lighting. The most economical is high pressure sodium. These lamps emit light over a continuous spectrum, but are biased towards a warm golden colour with consequent colour distortion. They are, however, suitable for outdoor areas, as they produce a pleasing environment in which buildings appear attractive. They are suitable for historic and conservation areas, and those of special architectural merit, and pedestrians are shown in acceptable colours.

An attractive light source is colour corrected mercury, which in a de-luxe form gives better colour rendering than high pressure sodium, but is twice as expensive: and four times as expensive as low pressure sodium. This light source has a characteristic cool white appearance. It is preferred by some people, but there are few places where the extra cost can be justified.

Tungsten and fluorescent tubular lamps must also be mentioned, but their use for practical purposes is very restricted. Due to their very high running costs, tungsten lamps should only be used in limited areas, where the closest reproduction of traditional gas lanterns is considered of sufficiently high importance to justify the extra cost.

Fluorescent tubular lamps should be confined to subways and special applications where for practical reasons a long narrow light source is necessary. Both tungsten and fluorescent tubular lamps can provide good colour rendering.

11.2 Subway lighting

Subways should be well lit in order to provide a pleasant environment by day and by night, and also to deter muggings and vandalism.

In order to provide light, the luminaires must survive intact. Cost is relative to performance. A cheap luminaire which is easily broken, is more expensive in the long run than one which may cost three times as much initially, but which is still working after the effects of atmosphere and vandalism.

UV stabilised polycarbonate is the only glazing material which should be used in subways and for low level luminaires at steps and ramped approaches, and this must be of a suitable thickness, either 3mm or 5mm, preferably 5mm. Clear sheet is stronger than opal, and flat sheet is stronger than any shape with exposed moulded corners. It must also be well supported, a broken lamp due to the polycarbonate flexing is still a victory to vandalism.

Luminaires must be of rugged construction and securely fixed. It is no use making them impregnable if they can be prised off the wall with a screwdriver, M10 ($\frac{3}{8}$'') rawl bolts or their equivalent should be used for fixings. Access to the interior of the luminaire must require special tools. This is rather unfortunate for maintenance men who forget their tools, but they are unlikely to do it more than once.

Surface luminaires are preferable to recessed types, because when a recessed luminaire reaches the end of its useful life, the maintenance department is usually faced with a hole in the wall which no available luminaire will fit.

Consideration should be given to the possible need for emergency lighting. This is necessary if the exits to the subways are not visible in the event of an electricity supply failure in the subway.

Standard GLC subway lighting fitting

110

150

lengths: 400
600
1000

11.3 Amenity lighting

Lighting under this heading includes all that for mainly pedestrian areas, but excludes subway, area and road lighting which is dealt with under separate headings.

The most important amenity areas are pedestrian precincts, large and small, and formal squares which often exist in towns and which are sometimes partly or wholly closed to traffic. Where traffic is not excluded safety, in relation to the traffic/pedestrian situation, must be given high priority.

In historic and conservation areas (see 18.1) the retention of the original lighting lanterns, or the provision of new 'replica' replacements of the original oil or gas lanterns with electric light sources, must be considered, if these are necessary for environmental reasons. In which case, the light output of the lanterns must be improved as much as possible commensurate with the total environment. A higher degree of glare will often be tolerated from these 'traditional' lanterns as an acceptable price to be paid for the retention of the old basic designs.

When 'traditional' lanterns are not considered essential and traffic is involved, an alternative to the usual road lighting luminaires can be considered without necessarily departing from the British Standard recommended form of road lighting. Lanterns are available for various mounting heights which are much more acceptable where the visual scene is important and justifies the additional expense involved.

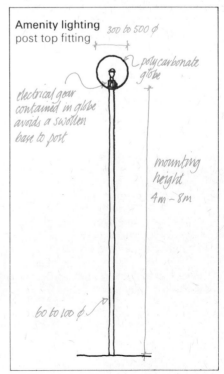

Amenity lighting post top fitting

300 to 500 ⌀

polycarbonate globe

electrical gear contained in globe avoids a swollen base to post

mounting height 4m – 8m

60 to 100 ⌀

historic post top fitting

copper lantern

450

1 m

2.7 m

cast iron post

Where traffic is excluded, or is restricted only to access, various forms of decorative lighting may be considered, depending upon the nature of the district from vandalism considerations. In some areas nothing but the most robust luminaires are likely to survive, but in other areas a luminaire has a reasonable chance of survival provided that it is out of reach and able to withstand a thrown missile. The most damaging of these likely to be encountered is a half brick, which can also prove to be a very useful test object. The glazing should be 3mm to 5mm thick UV stabilised polycarbonate which when used out of doors has a limited life expectation due to weathering, but nevertheless offers the longest expectation of trouble free life in a vandal prone area.

It is of little use employing a tough, relatively expensive, glazing material if it is not supported by a frame or body of adequate strength. It must also be remembered that polycarbonate is flexible and sufficient clearance must be provided so that the lamp does not suffer if a panel deflects due to a blow.

If the above-mentioned conditions are met, single lanterns or globes or clusters of these can be attractively arranged at intermediate mounting heights.

The lighting scheme should ensure that vertical surfaces are well lit, in order to form bright backgrounds, and covered walkways and canopies should have a system of local lighting units incorporated within their design.

11.4 Area lighting

Under this heading will be considered workaday lighting of open areas, which may exist between buildings in a housing complex or as open spaces in an urban environment.

There is little choice when the area is bounded by reasonably tall buildings. If floodlights can be mounted at not less than fourth floor level, this method of lighting will often be the most trouble free.

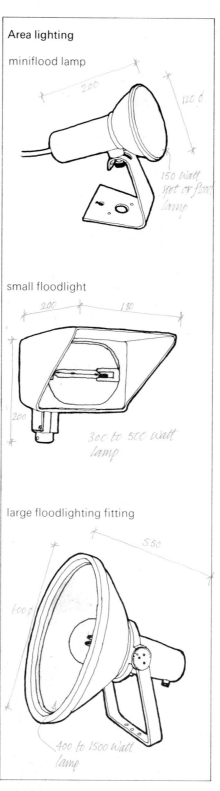

Area lighting

miniflood lamp

200

120.0

150 Watt spot or flood lamp

small floodlight

200

180

200

300 to 500 Watt lamp

large floodlighting fitting

550

400.0

400 to 1500 Watt lamp

The effects of floodlighting can be criticised as being too impersonal and stark, but the minimal maintenance which results is sometimes the overriding consideration. Furthermore, the absence of maintenance problems ensures that the floodlights are seldom out of lighting and this gives confidence to the user of the areas concerned.

If no adjacent buildings exist, or they are lower than four storeys, then either floodlights on 12m high columns will be necessary or the adoption of a lower mounting height, in which case either wall mounted lanterns or column mounted lanterns will have to be employed, or perhaps a combination of the two.

Wall mounted lanterns should be the first choice, as a good robust wall mounted lantern at 4m mounting height is likely to survive in preference to a post top lantern, but if the necessary walls are not available the post top lanterns will have to be used as a last resort. These are more vulnerable as, if they are not broken, the posts may be climbed and the lantern dismantled by vandals.

Illuminated bollards are sometimes used, but these are advised against, unless they are virtually unbreakable and have vandal-proof fastenings.

The other situation where post top or similar lanterns are often used is where, although the area is bounded by buildings on which floodlights can be mounted at a suitable height, the distance between buildings is excessive and some 'filling in' of the central area is necessary. The choice here is between floodlights on columns, or lower mounting height post top or similar lanterns. Usually the latter are preferred unless considerations of vandalism dictate high mounted floodlights.

11.5 Road lighting

This will usually follow the British Standard BS5489.

Where economy takes priority, low pressure sodium lamps should be used, but where a light source entailing a higher running cost can be justified on the grounds of better colour rendering, high pressure sodium lamps should be used. Areas justifying the use of these lamps include town centres, historic and conservation areas.

For normal traffic routes (BS5489 Part 2) up to 12m wide, a 10m mounting height seems appropriate to the scale of buildings usually encountered on these roads, but for wider roads carrying heavy traffic a 12m mounting height will usually be acceptable and beneficial in reducing the numbers of columns required. In large city squares, higher mounting heights can sometimes be used with advantage, thereby reducing still further the number of columns required.

In areas of particular visual importance it can be beneficial to employ lanterns other than those of conventional main road design, the shape of which seldom enhances the environment. It may be desired to avoid the need for road lighting columns in some areas, and where the necessary permissions can be obtained, wall mounted road lighting lanterns or floodlights may be employed. For a successful result, a moderately uniform frontage to the road is required, which enables a coherent lighting system to be installed.

It must be remembered that floodlighting of roads is outside the scope of the British Standard BS5489 Part 2, and care must be taken to ensure that the proposed installation fully complies with the requirements of the traffic.

Local distributor and access road lighting will usually follow the recommendation of the British Standard BS5489 Part 3 and employ 5m, 6m or 8m mounting height lanterns incorporating low pressure sodium lamps. If the area is considered of sufficient importance however, low wattage high pressure sodium lamps may be used.

It is recommended that all road lighting be controlled by light sensitive switches preferably of the electronic type. These may be either 'one part' or 'two part' pattern, the 'one part' being preferred except where its physical size would make it visually incongruous on a small lantern.

The policy of the Greater London

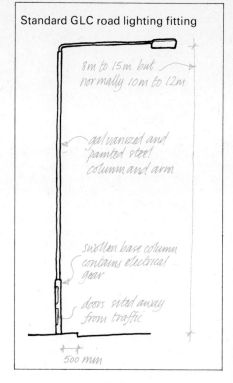

Standard GLC road lighting fitting

8m to 15m but normally 10m to 12m

galvanized and painted steel column and arm

swollen base column contains electrical gear

doors sited away from traffic

500 min

Council for metropolitan roads, is that road lighting columns should be of steel, shot or grit blasted, hot zinc sprayed, and protected by suitable sealer and primer with finishing coats applied after erection. Plastic coatings on columns have not yet been produced which are hard enough to withstand vandalism.

Sheet steel galvanised columns are not recommended in the relatively thin gauge normally used for road lighting.

11.6 High mast lighting

This form of lighting may be considered for roads where its special merits outweigh its usually higher cost.

It is particularly useful where several levels of road are present and at interchanges which occupy a large area, where conventional mounting height lighting columns would present a cluttered daytime appearance and a meaningless jumble of lights at night.

The mounting height will usually be 30m or more and the masts, often thick galvanised sheet steel, will support up to 6 or 8 lanterns. It is common practice to employ raising and lowering gear within the head frame and the mast in order to bring the lanterns, lamps and lamp control gear within easy reach of the ground.

Other applications of high mast lighting include large car parks and industrial areas.

The lanterns employed may be road lighting types, or floodlights for other applications.

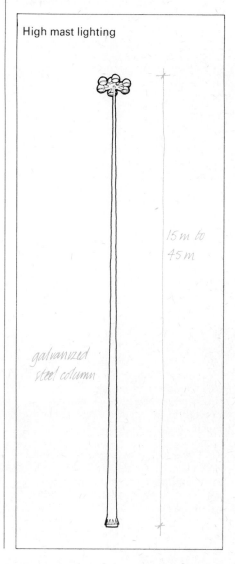

High mast lighting

15m to 45m

galvanized steel column

11.7 Underpass and short tunnel lighting

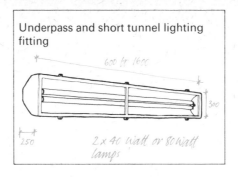

Underpass and short tunnel lighting
fitting

600 or 1600

300

250

2 x 40 Watt or 80 Watt
lamps

If these are short and straight and the exit can be seen on entering, artificial lighting may not be necessary in daytime.

If the exit cannot be seen from the entrance, artificial lighting will be necessary and should have two component parts. At the entrance there should be provided a relatively high level of lighting in daytime, about 3,000 lux, which should taper off to the basic level of lighting, about 200 lux, which will then continue at that level throughout the length of covered road.

A two-way covered road would normally be lit uniformly up to a length of about 150m. Where this length is exceeded both entrances will require the high level (3,000 lux) but this may be gradually reduced away from the entrances.

The reason for the high level of lighting at the entrance with a gradual reduction away from the entrance is, that whilst the eye can adapt from higher to lower illuminations, it requires time to do so.

The degree of reduction and the length of intermediate stages required, will depend upon the speed of the traffic and the overall length of the covered road.

Lighting in the entrance and intermediate zones can best be provided by high pressure sodium lamps, and in the basic zone by tubular fluorescent lamps in continuous rows. Where these are provided for daytime use, half lighting from the tubular fluorescent lamps will usually suffice at night.

If the covered section is part of a road unlit at night, it will not normally require any lighting itself after dark, but it may still require lighting during the daytime. If lighting is required at night, a uniform illumination should be provided throughout the length of the covered road.

Covered roads not requiring daytime lighting are normally short, but if night time lighting is necessary, individual floodlights giving a transverse distribution are usually employed at a space : height ration of 3:1.

High reflectance walls and, if possible, road surfaces should be provided, and the wall surface finish should be such that it can be easily cleaned : see 9.2 Underpasses.

In order to reduce visual contrast when approaching a covered road, a low reflectance finish should be provided on the portal surfaces, and also on the side walls, if any, of the approach.

Advice on all these matters can be found in BS5489 Part 7: 1971.

12.1 Public telephones

Public telephone boxes are installed and maintained by the Post Office.

They should be sited where they are conspicuous, but they should not obstruct pedestrians or interfere with visibility at bends or junctions. Where possible, they should be positioned away from the road at the backline of the footpath and, if space permits preferably behind the backline.

In order to minimise the effects of vandalism, telephone boxes should be sited where they are overlooked by houses, offices, busy roads, etc and where the street lighting is good.

If telephone boxes cannot be physically joined, and more than one are needed, a minimum space of 1m should be left clear all round each box. This enables the ground to be cleaned and the boxes to be maintained without too much difficulty.

The Post Office will install telephone equipment in structures not owned by them; bus shelters, kiosks and so on. In such cases they are only responsible for the maintenance of the telephone equipment.

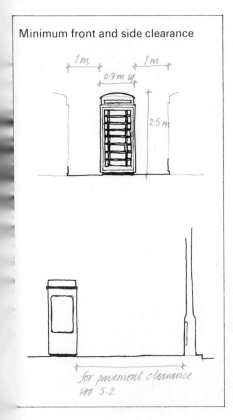

Minimum front and side clearance

for pavement clearance
see 5.2

Useful names (for addresses see chapter 21)
Post Office Telecommunications

12.2 Letter boxes

There are two types of letter box for public use. One is built into walls and the other is the free standing pillar box.

The wall mounted letter box is very useful where footpath space is limited. They are often found in Post Office walls or in brick or stone boundary walls, particularly where the urban environment has a rural emphasis.

Free-standing pillar boxes, painted post office red, make an invaluable contribution to the urban environment. They relate directly to the human scale and add a touch of friendliness to their surroundings – the cylindrical ones in particular.

Pillar boxes surviving from Queen Victoria's reign are still to be found in everyday use. The early mid-Victorian 'Penfold' boxes, where they survive in London, are statutorily listed by the DoE as being of special architectural or historic interest. Short of demolition by a passing vehicle, their removal has been effectively prevented and it is to be hoped that they are maintained so well that they never have to be retired to museums.

One cannot have too many pillar boxes, though the Post Office, being both suppliers and installers may not agree wholeheartedly.

In sighting pillar boxes, virtually the same requirements as those for telephone boxes apply, with the exception that pillar boxes are usually sited on the footpaths 0.5m from the kerb, whereas telephone boxes are preferably sited at or behind the backline of the footpath.

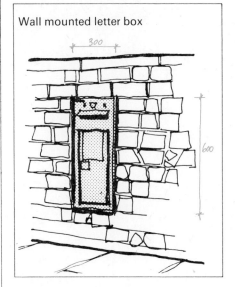

Wall mounted letter box

Pillar box

Mid-Victorian 'Penfold' pillar box

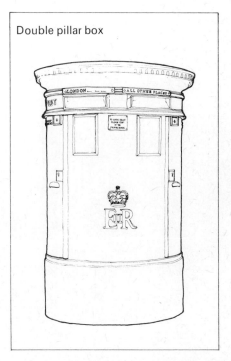

Double pillar box

12.3 Parking meters and ticket machines

On street parking is a problem in all urban environments. It can be left to its own devices or regulated by the use of yellow lines and related notices, and prepayment parking meters or 'pay and display' tickets.

Prepayment parking meters are installed at the kerb side of the footpath, one for each parking bay marked out in white lines on the road. To avoid clutter, two parking meters should share one post, wherever possible. Coins are inserted, which set a needle along a time scale and the clockwork mechanism of the meter returns it to zero. Thus the motorist can select the amount of time he requires up to the limit of the scale, usually 2 or 4 hours. After this time has elapsed, an excess charge is displayed followed by a penalty, both of which incur extra payments by the motorist.

Pay and display tickets are issued by an electrically powered machine, located close to the area to which it refers, for example, residents parking bays, car parks and marked out areas of road. The motorist, after inserting the correct fee, obtains a ticket for the period he requires. The ticket is printed with the week number, day and time, and is displayed on the inside of the vehicle windscreen.

Enforcement officers (policemen or parking wardens) patrol the parked vehicles and issue penalty notices, or worse, to motorists who infringe the parking regulations. The revenue produced by the meters and ticket machines can be put towards the cost of enforcement officers and the supply and maintenance of the meters and machines.

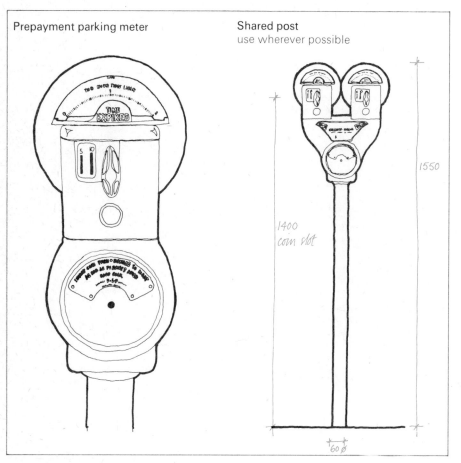

Prepayment parking meter

Shared post
use wherever possible

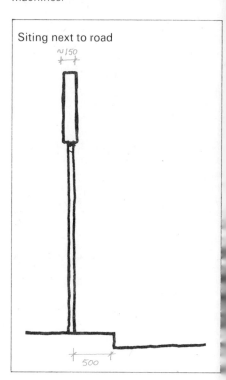

Siting next to road

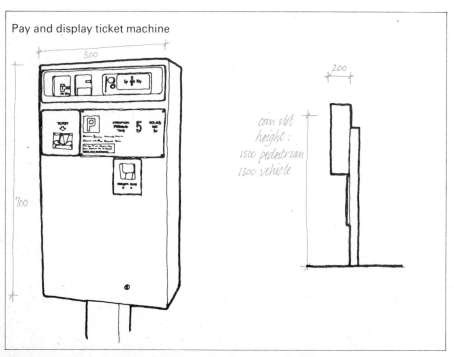

Pay and display ticket machine

Useful names (for addresses see chapter 21)
Control Systems Ltd
Fisher-Karpark Ltd
Setright Registers Ltd
The Universal Parking Meter Co Ltd

12.4 Underground services

In the urban environment, all manner of essential services go snaking about below ground. These underground services may be anywhere from 0.3m to 1.5m deep and their positions can be determined by finding lighting columns, inspection chambers, stop cocks etc which are usually directly above the services to which they relate.

Although it would be impracticable to rationalize the positions of existing services, it is important that they are accurately located and recorded on drawings.

For new or improved road building, it should be possible to accommodate services under the footpaths and verges, instead of under the road itself. Mains, laid in duplicate each side of the road, obviate the need for service connections across the road. If it is necessary for services to cross existing roads, they should be accommodated in thrust borings where possible, to avoid disturbing the road surface and the traffic.

Surface water and foul sewers are usually laid under the road, as they seldom need to be uncovered for repairs, but if space permits, consideration should be given to locating them under pavements, verges, continuous central refuges etc.

12.5 Overhead services

Where the cost of installing services underground is quite prohibitive, some services are carried overhead for example, Post Office telephone wires and domestic power cables.

It is preferable for services crossing roads to be accommodated in road bridges over the roads, usually in pipe bays. On new bridges over urban motorways, pipe bays or cable ducts adequate for future needs should be provided.

Where it is necessary for overhead pipes and cables to cross roads at points other than at bridges, they should be placed at heights suitable for their protection and the safety of the road traffic.

The minimum head clearance height is 5.5m.

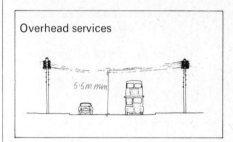

Overhead services

Mains should preferably be located in pavements as follows:

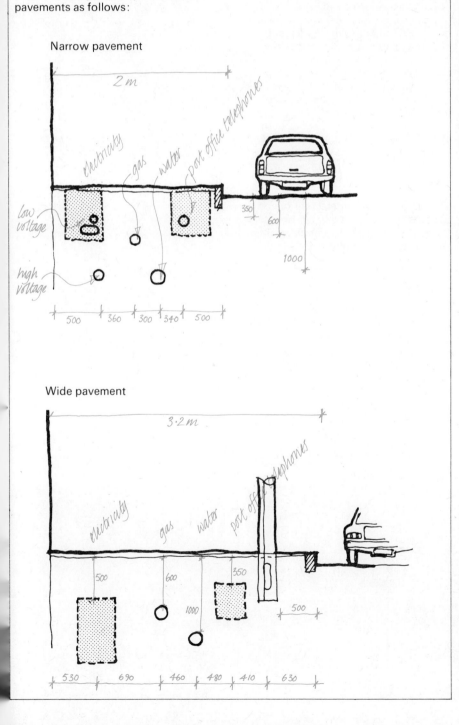

89

12.6 Electrical feeder pillars

Electrical fittings and fixtures in the urban environment require to be connected to a mains electricity supply, with its attendant dangers.

Whenever a connection has to be made to the mains supply cable, which can only be done by an electricity board engineer, a charge has to be paid to the electricity board.

In areas where many lights, illuminated bollards, etc are sited close together, it may well be more economical to install a feeder pillar containing several fused take off points for the lights, and only one supply mains connection: hence only one connection charge rather than many.

Feeder pillars are not particularly large and can be hidden away behind dwarf walls or planters with little difficulty, though access must be allowed at all times for maintenance.

Feeder pillars are generally made from pre-cast concrete or galvanised mild steel. They can be surface or root fixed. Inside each feeder pillar a marine-ply board is provided onto which the electrical equipment is secured.

Typical electrical feeder pillar

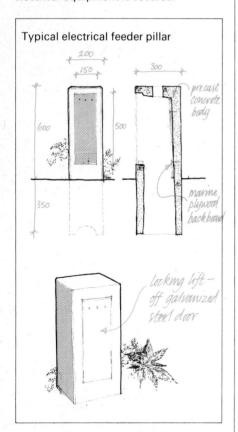

Useful names (for addresses see chapter 21)
Bergo Ltd
Concrete Utilities Ltd
Hale & Hale Engineers Ltd
Road Signs – Franco Ltd

12.7 Vehicle detectors/counters

In cities, it is advantageous if traffic volumes can be measured, both for control and planning purposes.

Vehicles can be counted by the use of a pneumatic rubber tube stretched across the road, which trips a digital readout every two axle crossings in a battery powered control box, usually strapped to a convenient lighting column. This sort of system is generally used on a temporary basis.

A more sophisticated, and more environmentally desirable method, is to use an electrical inductive loop detector. This consists of a loop of cable buried under the road surface which leads to a detector unit housed in a water-tight casing, which may be located at some distance away from the loop.

These detectors are sensitive to bicycles as well as vehicles and can be set to ignore the presence of parked vehicles.

The casing can preferably be mounted beneath the surface of the ground in a watertight chamber or on a pedestal 100mm diameter x 900mm high.

The signals from the detectors can be used to count traffic volumes, or be linked to traffic signal computers, either individually or centrally.

Typical vehicle detector/counters housed in underground chamber

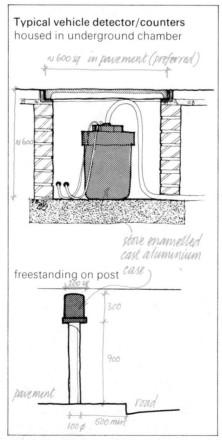

Useful names (for addresses see chapter 21)
GEC Elliot Traffic Automation Ltd
The Plessey Company Ltd.

CROSSINGS / SIGNALS

13.1 Traffic signals and controllers

In order to improve safety and lessen congestion, traffic signals are generally provided at busy road junctions.

The signal sequence is red, red/amber, green, amber.

Nowadays most traffic-signals are vehicle-actuated, but a few of the older fixed-time types can still be found.

Traffic signal controllers have many facilities and offer the traffic engineer great scope in controlling traffic, not the least of which is linking traffic lights to a central computer, which can determine ideal signalling phases continually throughout an area of control.

At signalled junctions, pedestrian crossings often have to be included. The crossings are marked out in studs on the road, in front of the stop line. Where turning traffic is light no special signal phases are needed. If, turning traffic is heavy, a pedestrian phase may be necessary, which halts all road traffic before pedestrians are signalled to cross: for pedestrian signals see 13.2.

The design of signal controlled junctions is best left to road and traffic engineers.

Temporary traffic signals

Temporary traffic signals are sometimes needed to control alternate single-lane flow, for example, at road works.

These signals can be activated by a microwave (radar) detector mounted on top of the signal head, which is pointed in the direction of the oncoming traffic and detects only those vehicles travelling towards it. Other vehicle detectors can be of the loop tapeswitch or air tube/diaphragm type. Fixed time and manual (hand) controllers may also be used.

The set of equipment usually needed at such sites consists of two three-light signal heads on portable stands, two vehicle detectors, two lengths of cable about 50m long and one control unit operating from 240 or 110 volts AC or 24–28 volts DC. If mains electricity is not available a generator is usually used to supply the necessary power.

The Ministry of Transport recommends that temporary traffic signals should always be vehicle-actuated, unless, for example, contractors' vehicles are likely to conflict with the through traffic in the controlled area, in which case, manual (hand) control should be used. In the event of failure of a vehicle detector, fixed time operation should be used.

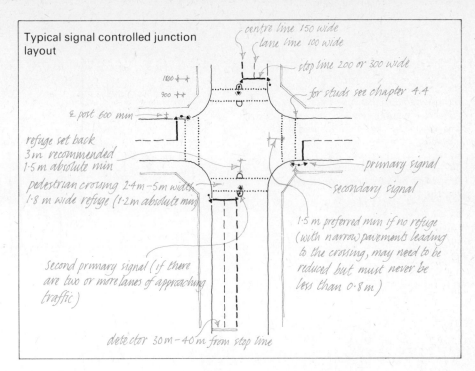

Typical signal controlled junction layout

centre line 150 wide
lane line 100 wide
stop line 200 or 300 wide
for studs see chapter 4.4
1800
900
& post 600 min
primary signal
secondary signal
refuge set back 3m recommended 1·5 m absolute min
pedestrian crossing 2·4m–5m width 1·8 m wide refuge (1·2m absolute min)
1·5 m preferred min if no refuge (with narrow pavements leading to the crossing, may need to be reduced but must never be less than 0·8 m)
second primary signal (if there are two or more lanes of approaching traffic)
detector 30 m – 40 m from stop line

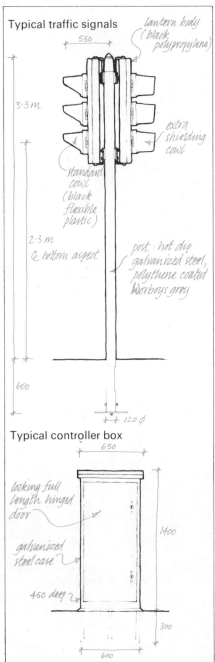

Typical traffic signals

lantern body (black polypropylene)
550
3·3 m
extra shielding cowl
standard cowl (black flexible plastic)
2·3 m & bottom aspect
post: hot dip galvanized steel, polythene coated Worboys grey
600
120 ∅

Typical controller box

650
locking full length hinged door
galvanized steel case
1400
450 deep
300
600

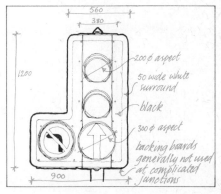

560
380
1200
200 ∅ aspect
50 wide white surround
black
300 ∅ aspect
backing boards generally not used at complicated junctions
900

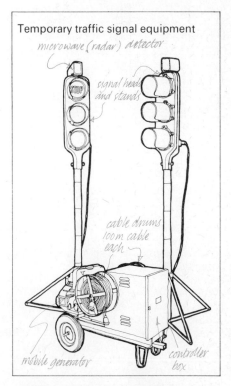

Temporary traffic signal equipment

microwave (radar) detector
signal heads and stands
STOP
cable drums 100m cable each
mobile generator
controller box

Useful names (for addresses see chapter 21)
Forest City Electric Co Ltd
GEC Ltd
George Pike Ltd
The Plessey Co Ltd

13.2 Pedestrian crossings

Where pedestrians have to cross busy roads between junctions, pedestrian crossings should be considered the first choice.

These crossings are either 'zebra' crossings or signal controlled 'pelican' crossings.

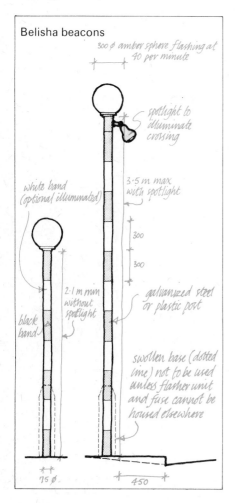

Belisha beacons

300 ⌀ amber sphere flashing at 40 per minute

spotlight to illuminate crossing

white band (optional illuminated)

3·5 m max with spotlight

300

300

2·1 m min without spotlight

galvanized steel or plastic post

black band

swollen base (dotted line) not to be used unless flasher unit and fuse cannot be housed elsewhere

75 ⌀

450

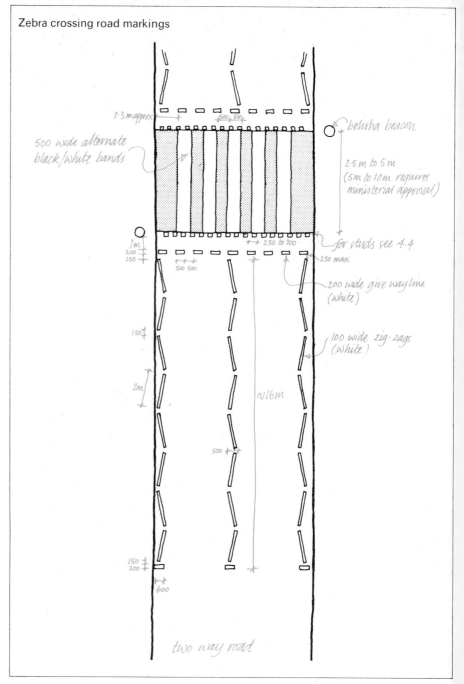

Zebra crossing road markings

1·3 m approx

500 wide alternate black/white bands

500 500

belisha beacon

2·5 m to 5 m (5m to 10m requires ministerial approval)

1m
200
150

2·50 to 700

for studs see 4.4

250 max

500 500

200 wide give way line (white)

150

100 wide zig-zags (white)

2m

~16m

500

150
200

600

two way road

Zebra crossings are indicated by alternate black and white bands across the road, edged with studs. A flashing Belisha beacon is positioned on the footpath or refuge, at the side of the crossing facing the oncoming traffic, where there is a refuge, each half counts as a separate crossing. A pedestrian, once he steps onto the crossing, has priority over motorised traffic.

When the number of pedestrians crossing the road exceeds 1000 per hour, a signal controlled 'Pelican' crossing is provided. In order to determine the number of pedestrians a survey has to be undertaken by the local authority, and often this is only instigated after pressure from residents associations, parents groups and the like.

Pelican crossings are marked out on the road with stainless steel non-reflective studs: for studs see 4.4.

Standard pedestrian traffic signals are used in place of the Belisha beacon at zebra crossings. The signals normally have vehicle priority and the pedestrian phase is brought in by pressing the button on the control box.

The signals showing to the pedestrian are either a red standing man or a green walking man, both against a black background. When the signals are in the pedestrian phase, a high pitched sound is emitted, for the benefit of visually handicapped pedestrians.

The signal sequence to traffic is: red, flashing amber, green, amber. During the flashing amber phase, vehicles must give way to any pedestrians wishing to cross, but may move over the crossing if it is clear.

When approach speeds are high, the installation of vehicle detectors enables the pedestrian phase only to be selected

during gaps in the traffic. This prevents an untimely pedestrian phase being made, which may give vehicles insufficient time to stop.

Useful names (for addresses see chapter 21)
Bergo Ltd
Forest City Electric Co Ltd
Hale & Hale Engineers Ltd
Pearce Gowshall Ltd
George Pike Ltd
The Plessey Co Ltd
Road Signs – Franco Ltd

Pelican crossing signals

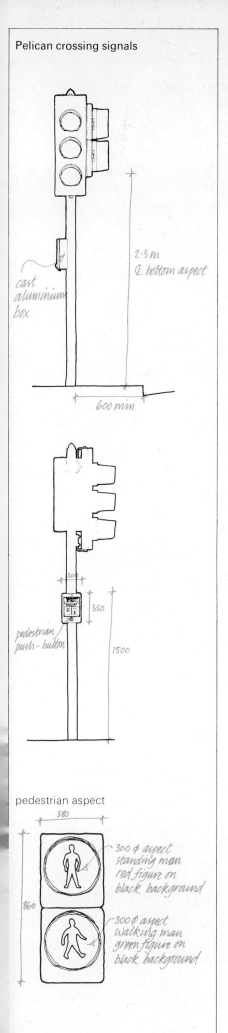

2·3 m
℄ bottom aspect

cast
aluminium
box

600 min

200

350

pedestrian
push-button

1500

pedestrian aspect

380

860

300 ⌀ aspect
standing man
red figure on
black background

300 ⌀ aspect
walking man
green figure on
black background

Pelican crossing road markings

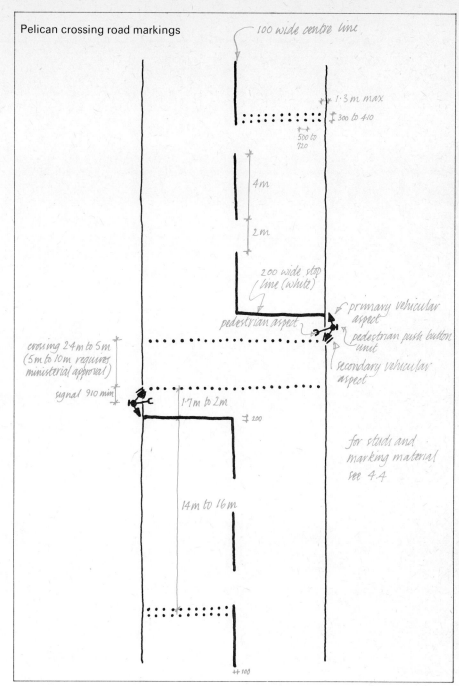

100 wide centre line

1·3 m max

300 to 410

500 to
720

4m

2m

200 wide stop
line (white)

pedestrian aspect

primary vehicular
aspect

pedestrian push button
unit

secondary vehicular
aspect

crossing 2·4 m to 5 m
(5m to 10m requires
ministerial approval)

signal 910 mm

1·7m to 2m

⊐ 200

for studs and
marking material
see 4.4

14m to 16m

100

Signs/ advertising/ information

The urban environment is absolutely peppered with information of one sort or another.

Traffic signs for the motorist which seem to be proliferating rapidly; pedestrian signs for pedestrians, which regrettably seem to be disappearing fast. Hoardings, poster boards, name signs and placards for commercial advertising, all of which can be a major contributor to urban clutter. The advertiser, in the interests of himself or his clients, attempts to place as many advertisements as he can "where folk can't miss'em". This is contrary to the aims of the environmental designer who tries to integrate areas with no single feature being over-dominant.

To a large degree, advertising is essential and desirable in the urban environment, and if incorporated at the design stage of a scheme can prove to be a colourful and interesting feature.

Public information (notice boards, bus information, pedestrian signs, town maps, street finders, etc) is usually much easier to integrate into the environment, as it is all to a much smaller scale than commercial advertising.

Each display of information of road signs, advertising and public information should be assessed on the grounds of its necessity, size and siting. Perhaps the most important question to be asked is: Is it really necessary?

14.1 Traffic signs/ secret signs

Traffic signs

Traffic signs are necessary for the safe, smooth passage of road traffic. They should ideally tell the motorist what he must or must not do, where he is, and which direction he should take to reach his destination.

All signs should conform to the appropriate statutory instruments and recommendations issued by the Department of Transport. The 'Traffic Signs Manual' is one such example, and for further information these publications must be consulted.

or on which the display of information may be altered, usually to an alternative.

There are two basic types. The information is changed either by mechanical means, or by altering the internal lighting.

Mechanical devices vary from a single hand-operated flap, which has two positions to change the information, to a complex arrangement of rotating or sliding shutters or blinds activated by timers and electric motors.

Internally illuminated 'secret' signs generally show a blank sign face when not illuminated, and reveal a message when they are lit, though many 'secret' signs are exceedingly difficult to read, especially if the sun is shining on them.

Part time signs are often used in connection with tidal flows, bridge openings, car parks, etc.

The maintenance of part time signs must be to a high quality, particularly if the signs are complicated.

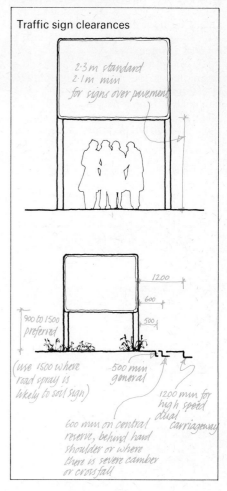

Traffic sign clearances

2·3 m standard
2·1 m min
for signs over pavement

1200
600
500
900 to 1500 preferred
(use 1500 where road spray is likely to soil sign)
500 mm general
1200 min for high speed dual carriageway
600 mm on central reserve, behind hard shoulder or where there is severe camber or crossfall

Standard flag type sign

sheet aluminium sign face)

Newmarket 56 (A11)
Chelmsford 28 (A12)

painted galvanized steel R H S post and sign frame

access door

Signs can be internally or externally illuminated, or have non-illuminated plain or reflective faces.

The Greater London Council has designed a range of externally illuminated direction signs supported on rectangular hollow section steel posts. Sign faces with areas up to 9m² can be cantilevered from a single post, larger sign areas require two posts.

The signs are bolted down onto prepared foundations which allow easy replacement should it become necessary. Bridging foundations are available for positions where it is required to site a post directly above shallow underground services.

Part time signs

Part time signs are those which only display information for part of the time,

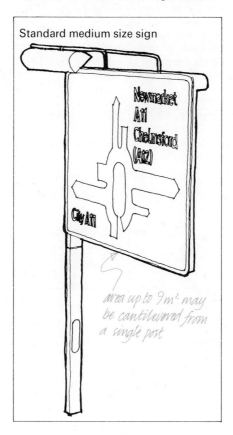

Standard medium size sign

Newmarket
A11
Chelmsford
(A12)

City A11

area up to 9m² may be cantilevered from a single post

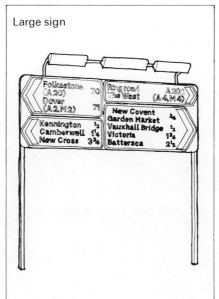

Large sign

Folkestone (A20) 70
Dover (A2,M2) 71
Ring road The West (A4,M4) A20
Kennington ½
Camberwell 1¼
New Cross 3¾
New Covent Garden Market ¾
Vauxhall Bridge ½
Victoria 1¾
Battersea 2¼

Useful names (for addresses see chapter 21)
Berger Traffic Markings Ltd
Bergo Ltd
Bribex Ltd (S)
Burnham Signs Ltd
Claudgen Traffic Signs Ltd (S)
Eleco Ltd
Forest City Signs Ltd (S)
Glasdon Ltd
Greater London Council
Haldo Developments (T)
Hale & Hale Engineers Ltd (T)
Hawesigns Ltd
Hills (Patents) Ltd (T)
3M Co Ltd
Pearce Gowshall Ltd (S)
Pearce Signs Ltd (S) (T)
Road Signs – Franco Engineers Ltd (T)
G Tipper & Co Ltd (T)

Temporary signs for road works, etc
Bribond Signs Ltd
Fairway Technical Plastics Ltd
Finalite Company Ltd
Harold Bloom Signs (Sales) Ltd
Parkinson Richmark Safety Products

(S) = Secret signs in addition to traffic signs
(T) = Temporary signs in addition to traffic signs

14.2 Gantries

Gantries are structures designed to support illuminated overhead traffic signs. They are used over roads where traffic is heavy and roadside signs may well be obliterated for a lot of the time.

Overhead signs are particularly useful in indicating lanes at busy junctions and on urban motorways.

The signs may be internally illuminated or externally illuminated. Internal illumination is preferred in urban areas, being both easier to read at night and less obtrusive by day.

The gantry structure should be as simple and light as possible.

The Greater London Council has designed two types of gantry for use on its roads either having 'A' frame or vertical leg supports.

The method of servicing the gantry must be agreed with the police before detail design work begins. Servicing can be either from a service hoist parked on the road, or from a cat-walk on the gantry. The GLC prefers servicing by hoists for reasons of cost and convenience.

Catwalks should be completely enclosed by continuous handrails. On the GLC designed externally illuminated gantry, where the catwalk is in front of the sign-face, eye bolts are fixed along the sign face into which safety harnesses worn by maintenance personnel may be attached. This enables the handrail to be dispensed with in front of the sign face and the sign to be lowered, thus reducing its bulk.

Wherever it is convenient, overhead signs may be mounted on bridges over the road. This obviates the need for a special gantry, and saves a great deal of time and money.

14.3 Pedestrian signs

Pedestrian signs are for the use of pedestrians on routes separate from motor traffic routes.

This seems to have been forgotten by the majority of sign designers and manufacturers. Nowadays most pedestrian signs are merely scaled down versions of traffic signs, with destinations stacked one on top of another and arrows pointing left, right and centre.

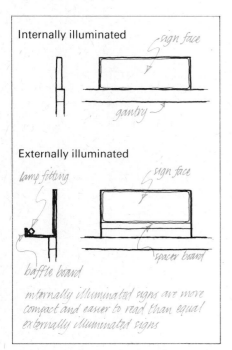

Internally illuminated

sign face

gantry

Externally illuminated

lamp fitting

sign face

spacer board

baffle board

internally illuminated signs are more compact and easier to read than equal externally illuminated signs

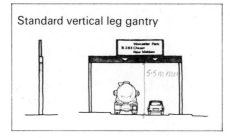

Standard vertical leg gantry

Worcester Park
B 283 Cheam
New Malden

5·5 m min

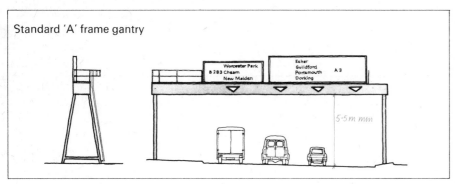

Standard 'A' frame gantry

Worcester Park
B 283 Cheam
New Malden

Esher
Guildford
Portsmouth
Dorking

A 3

5·5 m min

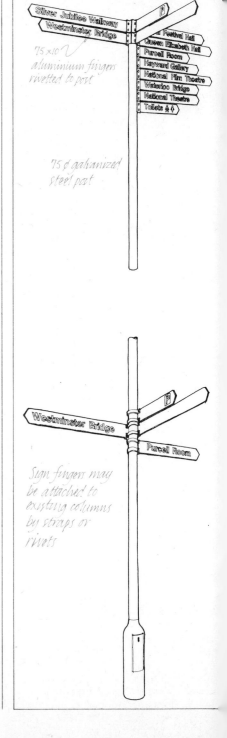

Typical finger-post pedestrian sign

Silver Jubilee Walkway
Westminster Bridge

Royal Festival Hall
Queen Elizabeth Hall
Purcell Room
Hayward Gallery
National Film Theatre
Waterloo Bridge
National Theatre
Toilets

75 x 10 aluminium fingers rivetted to post

75 ø galvanized steel post

Westminster Bridge

Purcell Room

Sign fingers may be attached to existing columns by straps or rivets

Useful names (for addresses see chapter 21)
British Steel Corporation   *Tubes Division*
Claudgen Ltd
I G Engineering Ltd
Road Signs – Franco Ltd
South Coast Welders Ltd

A traffic sign is designed to be read by a moving motorist approaching from one direction. It is, therefore, an advantage if all traffic signs have the same legibility and appearance which can be assimilated as quickly as possible.

Pedestrian signs, on the other hand, may usually be approached from any direction, stopped at, walked round, examined minutely and subjected to anything a pedestrian might feel free to do. Pedestrian signs can be used not only to give directions, but also to give identity to an area, and this provides a useful method for introducing colour and interest into the environment.

The simplest and most direct way of giving directions is to point directly towards the destination and a finger sign does exactly that.

It is recommended that where pedestrian signs are required, finger signs should be used. They can be attached to their own posts or to existing lighting columns and structures.

The sign fingers may be plain, pierced, illuminated, ornamented, coloured, thick, thin; in fact virtually anything, so there is no excuse for providing mini-traffic signs.

The sign fingers should be capable of being attached to existing lighting columns and structures.

14.4 Street name plates/boundary signs

Street name plates are used to identify streets and roads and are a very necessary feature of the urban environment.

They give a sense of 'place' and 'identity' to an area. It is more human and friendly to live in, say, Woodside Road, than it is to live in West 32nd Street, despite numerical indexing being a much easier system to use.

Street name plates used to be highly individual; painted on walls, finger posts, boards, set in tiles, carved in timber, carved in stone and so on, in a variety of sizes and lettering.

Unfortunately, nowadays, the Ministry of Transport recommendations have reduced the choice of lettering to two, either the revised MoT or Kindersley. Both are all capitals, MoT is 75mm or 100mm high sans-serif and Kindersley is 89mm high with serifs.

The plates are normally made from stove enamelled pressed, or cast aluminium or vitreous enamelled mild steel, having black lettering and border on a white background.

The sign-plates are backed with marine plywood which can be fixed to posts, walls, etc. All fixing should be vandal resistant and treated to withstand corrosion.

Boundary signs

Boundary signs are similar to street name plates except that they identify the boundaries of areas. 'Barnsley welcomes careful drivers' and 'You are now leaving Barnsley' being fairly typical examples of the homilies often combined with the place names.

Even though the lettering used today is MoT, boundary signs can lend themselves to flights of imagination, incorporating multi-coloured coats of arms and humourous messages, all of which should be encouraged, within sensible limits.

Typical boundary sign

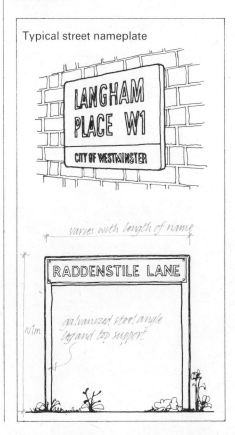

Typical street nameplate

Useful names (for addresses see chapter 21)
Dymo Ltd
Greater London Council
Milton Keynes Development Corporation

Useful names (for addresses see chapter 21)
Burnham Signs Ltd
Pearce Signs Ltd
G Tipper & Co Ltd
Ward & Co Ltd

14.5 Bus/train signs

The main purpose of bus and train signs is to help people find their way to these forms of transport, or from one to another.

Direction signs to buses and trains should be in accordance with MoT recommendations and regulations and use standard symbols: see 'Traffic Signs Manual.'

Bus stop signs mark the assembly point for passengers for a particular route, show the bus driver where to stop, and warn other drivers that they should not obstruct that area. The sign should be high enough to be seen over the tops of most vehicles and cause minimum obstruction to motorists sight lines.

The bus stop sign normally carries the bus symbol, the name or symbol of the bus company, the route numbers, whether it is a fare stage or request stop, and which side to queue. An additional panel is often provided at a lower level on the same post on which timetables are displayed.

Bus stop signs are made in stove enamelled aluminium or vitreous enamelled mild steel. They may be fixed to lighting columns, if one happens to be sited at the right place, or to their own posts. These may be galvanised and painted mild steel tubing, painted aluminium tubing, timber, or, as in London, reinforced precast concrete.

British Rail

British Rail and London Transport underground railway

Standard bus sign

The precast concrete though being initially more expensive, has been found to be virtually maintenance free. All concrete posts erected in public places should be suitably reinforced such that after any vehicular impact, they will not become possible lethal projectiles.

Bus stop signs may be combined with bus shelters. At such places it is desirable if the name of the bus stop is displayed.

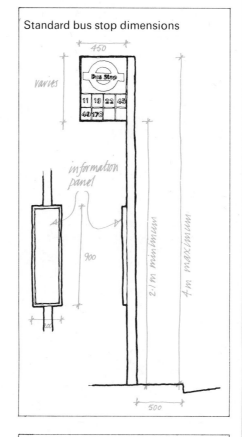

Standard bus stop dimensions

Bus stop incorporated into bus shelter

Useful names (for addresses see chapter 21)
Burnham Signs

14.6 Maps/street finders/ information

In urban environments it is very helpful to display town maps and street finders. These are often combined with public information boards and sited at points where people gather; bus stations, railway stations, town halls, squares, gardens, etc.

They are normally printed on a roller-blind which is contained in an illuminated weather and vandal resistant case. The blind can be revolved, by the use of handwheels, which enables a lot of information to be displayed in a small area.

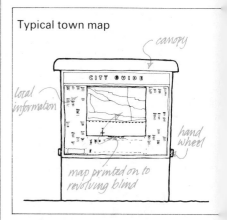

Typical town map

The Greater London Council has produced some curved three dimensional maps of the South Bank area made in glass reinforced concrete (grc) on a polystyrene foam core. If an authority already has a scale-model of an area, it is quite simple to make a rubber mould from it and cast a copy in grc.

Curved three dimensional relief map of South Bank (glass reinforced cement)

Public information: local authority posters, public notices, local events posters, etc. are usually displayed on boards headed by the name of the public authority to which they relate. These boards can be fixed on posts or walls, are normally made from timber, aluminium and steel and require annual repainting and occasional replacement.

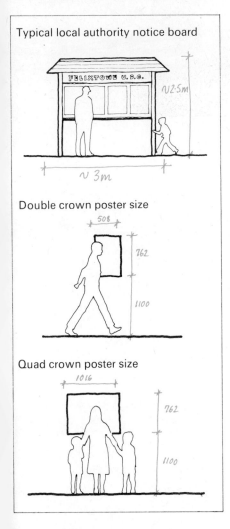

Typical local authority notice board

Double crown poster size

Quad crown poster size

As part of the GLC range of co-ordinated street furniture (see 19.0) a freestanding glass reinforced cement curved poster board has been designed which can display 2 four sheet (1524 x 1016mm) posters or 4 quad crown posters or 8 double crown posters.

The grc is natural mould finish and the board is maintenance free. The name or logo is pierced right through the top of the board.

Another item in the GLC co-ordinated range of street furniture is a grc quad crown poster board which is maintenance free and can be fixed to walls or posts. This board takes two double crown posters or one quad crown poster.

Useful names (for addresses see chapter 21)
Burnham Signs Ltd
City Guides Ltd
Greater London Council
London & Provincial Poster Group Ltd
Mills & Allen Ltd

Curved free standing 4 sheet poster board, 1.5m radius (glass reinforced cement)

4 double crown, 2 quad crown or 1 four sheet poster (pasted on)
50 projection front and back
100 thick GRC/polystyrene/GRC sandwich

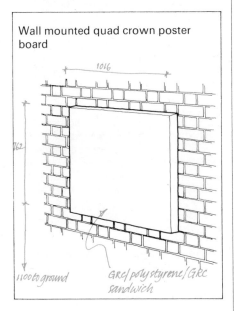

Wall mounted quad crown poster board

1100 to ground
GRC/polystyrene/GRC sandwich

14.7 Advertising/posters

Commercial advertising can enhance, or be a blight on an environment. It is up to the environmental designer and planner to ensure that any advertising is used in a positive way.

Poster hoardings spaced along a close boarded timber fence are infinitely preferable to the rusting corrugated iron fencing which so often surrounds building sites.

A freestanding circular poster drum is better than posters stuck onto shop windows in shopping areas.

Clean and well maintained bus shelters carrying advertising are better than the usual bus shelters with broken panels and piles of litter on the roofs.

Litter bins with advertisements, mounted on lighting columns, are better than no litter bins at all.

Commercial advertising can produce useful income for local authorities. In a highly desirable location such as Oxford Street, London, a single poster drum can bring in a rental of something like £1000 a year. Advertising companies also have schemes whereby they will install and maintain small environmental areas, including furniture and planting, so long as some advertising is included. As these areas may be designed by the local authorities, this is a very useful way to improve the environment at no cost to the authority.

Posters and hoardings are available in standard sizes. Large hoardings are either posted with many standard size posters butted together to form one large image, or are hand-painted by poster-artists.

Internally illuminated poster cabinets contain posters sandwiched between sheets of acrylic, housed in locking frames and lit from behind.

Poster boards which are not internally illuminated are preferably faced with galvanised sheet steel. This enables the poster paste to adhere well and the poster to be scraped off, after having been soaked with water, without damage to the surface.

The supporting framework is mainly constructed from timber with extruded aluminium trim or galvanised and painted steel.

If commercial advertising is to be included in any environmental scheme, advertising companies should be consulted at the earliest opportunity. They may well be able to provide help, in a number of ways, which might be used to add to the scope and interest of the scheme as a whole.

4 sheet poster dimensions

1016
1524
~400

16 sheet poster dimensions

2030
3050
~1000
increase in multiples of 2030

48 sheet poster dimensions

6090
3050
~1000

14.8 Commercial name signs

As with advertising, name signs can have a constructive or detrimental effect on an area.

They are used to identify commercial concerns; shops, offices, factories, stadiums, garages, etc, and obviously in the interests of commerce, should be as large and strident as possible.

The environmental designer will rarely be able to have any influence on the design of these signs, except where planning permission is required before they can be erected. In such cases, before planning permission is granted, the sign in relation to the surroundings should be considered carefully. If the sign would in any way detract from the wholeness of the area, it should be redesigned until it harmonizes with its surroundings.

This close examination of design proposals happens as a matter of course in conservation areas and areas of special importance, but if one looks at the average shopping high street one cannot see evidence of the same attention to detail. A common occurrence is a beautiful ornate Victorian façade covered over with huge areas of garish internally illuminated acrylic sheeting, or well proportioned small shop fronts, knocked together to form a huge emporium of commerce totally out of scale with its surroundings. Regrettably this list is endless.

Any area where people live or circulate is important.

If an area does not have any special features to give it an immediate identity, more attention must be given to detail design and the integration of the separate elements into a whole.

Name signs can be made in virtually any style, size or material. They may be internally or externally illuminated; it is very rare for a name sign not to be illuminated in some way.

Historically, name signs were either hand painted or carved and painted into fascia boards, gates, doors, etc. This practice preserved the integrity of the building, however humble.

Applied individual letters can be used in a similar way and are infinitely preferable to internally illuminated panel signs which are the 'soft option'.

Projecting signs and symbols such as pub signs and shop signs can be used to good effect, and provide interesting features, particulalry where long linear blocks of buildings stretch way into the distance with no horizontal projections or details.

Shop sign
illuminated projecting symbol can be used to good effect
individual letters applied to shop front

Projecting sign
adds colour and interest
COUTTS & CO. BANKERS

Structures

In the urban environment, there is often the need to provide kiosks, shelters, awnings, toilets, etc.

Historically, a large variety of permanent and semi-permanent free-standing structures have evolved, some very notable, others of no particular merit: Victorian 'cabby' shelters, ornate cast-iron lavatories, street vendors sheds and booths, toll booths, police telephone boxes, awnings, sun blinds and so on.

Again, as with the original pillar boxes, the Victorian Cabmen's shelters in London are now protected by the DoE as buildings of special architectural or historic interest. No doubt in time, other relics will follow the same course if they survive long enough.

Regrettably, as the needs of people have changed over the years, many of these interesting and unique structures have completely disappeared: the last horse-drawn cabby in London retired in 1947, police constables use personal radios instead of police telephone boxes, and toll-booths are now very few and far between.

There is no reason to suppose that the calls of nature are any different now than they were when public lavatories were plentiful in towns and cities, so why have so many disappeared? The usual answer is that one can always visit a shop or a pub, only they are closed more than half the time. It is desirable and sometimes very necessary, to include public lavatories in any new environmental scheme.

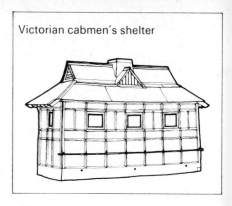

Victorian cabmen's shelter

Police telephone box

15.1 Kiosks

Kiosks and booths are provided for the use of gatemen, security officers, street vendors, car park attendants and so on. (For telephone kiosks see 12.1). Where money or goods are to be stored the kiosk or booth must be relatively secure and vandal resistant.

Until the advent of glass reinforced plastics (grp), most kiosks were made from timber with glass windows and weather-proofed with anything from 'roofing felt' to paint. Modern kiosks are almost without exception made from grp, though experimental kiosks are being developed in glass reinforced cement.

The smaller kiosks are usually supplied as a complete unit, the larger ones are constructed from modular sections assembled on site.

The only site work necessary for installing a GRP kiosk, is that of preparing a reinforced concrete slab of a suitable size and thickness for the kiosk, and the supply of services as required.

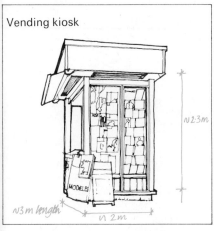
Vending kiosk

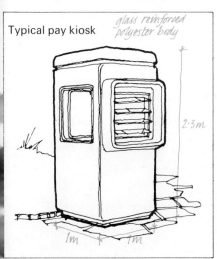
Typical pay kiosk

Useful names (for addresses see chapter 21)
Glasdon Ltd
Norman and Sons (Marketing) Ltd
Sinclair (Contract Furnishers) Ltd
Town and Country Steelcraft Ltd
Urban Enviroscape Ltd

15.2 Shelters/ covered walkways

Shelters are provided for the use of the general public, mainly to protect them from the elements.

There are two main types; short stay for use while waiting for transport, etc, or long stay, where seats are provided for sitting to look at the view or simply to have a rest and a chat.

In the urban environment the majority of shelters are provided for the use of people queueing for buses. In the past, London Transport was the sole supplier and maintainer of bus shelters in London. More lately, shelters are being provided by Advertising Companies who supply, install and maintain shelters, some of which contain four-sheet advertisements, at no cost to the local authority or the bus company: see 14.7 commercial advertising.

Shelters containing seating are usually only found in pedestrian areas, parks, gardens, squares and in the more rural parts of the urban environment.

Covered walkways (shopping arcades are outside the scope of this manual) usually consist of short stay shelter units fixed together to cover the length of a walkway. In Europe and America, pedestrianised streets have been covered by large shelter structures, but so far, nothing on this scale has been put up in Brittain.

At sites where glazing is particularly vulnerable to vandalism, it is better to use clear polycarbonate plastic sheet instead of glass.

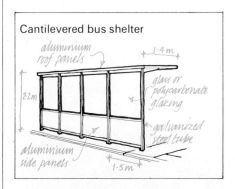
Cantilevered bus shelter

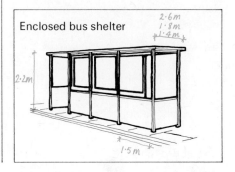
Enclosed bus shelter

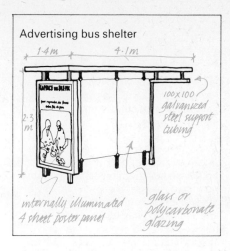
Advertising bus shelter

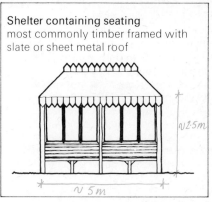
Shelter containing seating
most commonly timber framed with slate or sheet metal roof

Covered walkway
construction as bus shelter

Useful names (for addresses see chapter 21)
Abacus Municipal Ltd
Adshell Ltd
Field Engineering (Field Aircraft Services Ltd)
Mills & Allen Ltd
Milton Keynes Development Corporation
Norman and Sons (Marketing) Ltd
Sinclair (Contract Furnishers) Ltd
Town and Country Steelcraft Ltd
Urban Enviroscape Ltd

15.3 Awnings/sunblinds

Awnings and sunblinds are used to give temporary protection from the elements, including the sun.

They are made from canvas or woven plastics, supported by wire, metal or timber frames. Awnings and sunblinds provide a very good and cheap way of introducing colour into the urban environment. They relate well to the human scale and can become very strong features in the street scene, for example the sunblinds of 'Harrods' store in Knightsbridge, London.

Awnings
Awnings are nothing more than roof canopies supported by posts either guyed with wires or let into sockets set in the ground. Abroad, they are often used, in conjunction with glass screen wind-breaks, as summer extensions to cafés, restaurants, bars or similar, but this practise is not common in Britain, perhaps because of our climate.

In areas where space is at a premium, awning support posts should be let into sockets in the ground; wire guys can be highly dangerous to the unwary, disabled or blind.

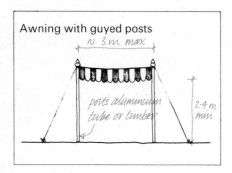

Awning with guyed posts
~ 3 m max
posts aluminium tube or timber
2·4 m min

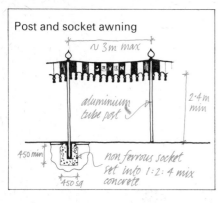

Post and socket awning
~ 3 m max
aluminium tube post
2·4 m min
450 min
non ferrous socket set into 1:2:4 mix concrete
450 sq

Sunblinds
Sunblinds are usually cantilevered from the side of buildings to shade windows and when large enough, to provide protection for café extensions and additional vending areas.

There are two types of sunblind in common use, the straight roller blind or the 'dutch' or continental blind which may be hinged or fixed.

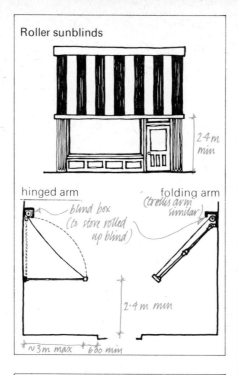

Roller sunblinds
2·4 m min

hinged arm
blind box (to store rolled up blind)

folding arm (trellis arm similar)

2·4 m min
~ 3 m max
600 min

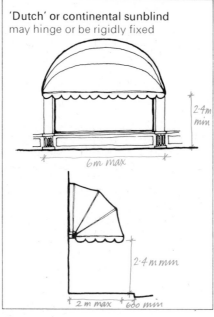

'Dutch' or continental sunblind
may hinge or be rigidly fixed
2·4 m min
6 m max

2·4 m min
2 m max
600 min

Awnings and sunblinds can be very useful in bringing colour to the urban scene. They relate well to human scale and are not expensive.

Wherever possible, the environmental designer would do well to introduce awnings and sunblinds, particularly in newly pedestrianised areas. If the buildings are privately owned, it often does not require much persuasion on the part of the designer to convince the owners of the value of blinds, particularly when commercial name signs are on them.

Useful names (for addresses see chapter 21)
Benjamin Edgington Ltd
(Blacks of Greenock)
Deans Blinds
Electromatic Sunblinds Ltd
Mitco Blinds
Perma Blinds Ltd
Piggott Bros & Co Ltd

15.4 Public conveniences

In public places people often need to use a lavatory.

In an endeavour to meet this need, public lavatories have been provided by the authorities since at least Roman times. In AD 315 there were 1,444 public lavatories in Rome, and the Roman Empire was well provided for, even in London.

After the collapse of the Roman Empire, public lavatories were limited to sites above running water, this happy situation pertained throughout the Middle Ages. It was not until the establishment of main sewer systems in the mid 19th Century, that public lavatories began to be found in city and town centres.

Early Victorian lavatories were free standing cast-iron structures not dissimilar to the splendid ornate French pissoirs; but these are now exceedingly rare.

In the late 19th Century, public lavatories started to disappear underground, the only visible mark of their presence being the entrances, which were usually surrounded by ornate iron railings with polished brass handrails and fittings; in London, Leicester Square has a good example of this type.

Over the years, many public lavatories have been vandalised or fallen into a state of disrepair and have been closed or filled in. It seems rather ironic that as the rate of population and tourism has boomed, the number of public lavatories has dwindled. Mean local authorities must assume that lavatory attendants are dispensible, which is far from the case.

If this inconvenient state of affairs is not to continue, the environmental designer should make sure that any remaining 'Temples of convenience' are restored, and that every new environmental scheme has its own public lavatory if there is not one nearby.

16.1 Litter bins

Public places are often plagued by litter. With the increase in pre-packaging, people have more rubbish to discard and there is a real need for litter bins to be provided in all public places.

Considering the large number of manufacturers who produce litter bins, it is amazingly difficult to find a bin when one is needed. Even when a bin is found, it is all too often full to overflowing and surrounding by a pile of litter on the ground.

The presence of litter has a marked deteriorative effect on any environment; it harbours dirt and disease, it is unsightly and frequently smells.

Litter bins should be sited at obvious points in public places such as; seating areas; where queues of people collect; major pedestrian routes; and shopping areas particularly outside tobacconists, sweet and food shops.

Litter bins should cause the minimum of obstruction whilst being visually prominent. The size of litter bins must be appropriate to the frequency with which it is emptied. Large bins tend to encourage the dumping of household rubbish, and so on. As a rule, many small bins are preferable to a few large bins. Large bins should contain separate liners small enough to be lifted, when full, by one person.

British Standard litter bins (see 20) are available in four size ranges, the capacities being measured in litres:

Type A: 14 litres to 28 litres (0.5 ft³ to 1 ft³)
Type B: 28 litres to 85 litres (1 ft³ to 3 ft³)
Type C: 85 litres to 170 litres (3 ft³ to 6 ft³)
Type D: Over 170 litres (over 6 ft³)

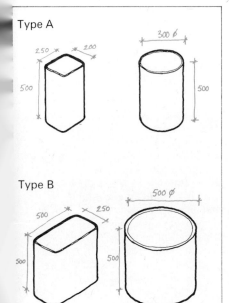

Type A

Type B

Type C

Type D

Type D

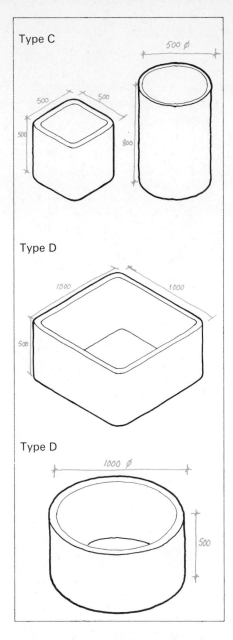

Litter bins must be made from materials which withstand heavy use and abuse; for example precast concrete, glass reinforced concrete, heavy gauge steel and aluminium, low density polyethylene plastic and timber.

The best bin finishes are obviously those which resist vandalism, scratching with sharp instruments, blows from blunt instruments and fire when the contents are set alight.

The only bins which will withstand fire without untoward effects are those made from precast concrete and glass reinforced concrete. Stainless steel and aluminium discolour badly, paint and plastic finishes burn off, and plastic melts away or ignites.

Bins can be freestanding or fixed to posts or walls. The fixings should be particularly robust and unless freestanding bins are temporary, they should be firmly secured to the ground. Out of thirty six precast concrete litter bins, each weighing over fifty kilogrammes, sited along the South Bank of the Thames in London, only five

remained after a few months; the rest had been lifted over the river-wall and hurled into the river.

Timber is usually treated with a clear preservative to enhance the qualities of the wood, unless a hardwood is used which requires no preservative treatment, such as, teak, iroko, afrormosia and so on. Teak has the advantage of being immune from attack by white ants!

To empty the litter, small bins are usually designed to be lifted off their mountings or to be swivelled upside down. For large bins it is often necessary to provide the bins with a removable liner. These are usually made from wire mesh or galvanised sheet steel. In practice it is preferable to use galvanised sheet steel liners, as even a small wire mesh allows some rubbish to fall through into the bottom of the outer container, which in some bins is exceedingly difficult to reach and clean out.

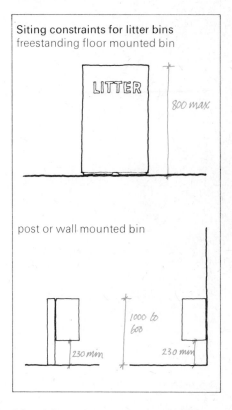

Siting constraints for litter bins
freestanding floor mounted bin

LITTER

800 max

post or wall mounted bin

1000 to 600

230 min   230 min

Often it is necessary to secure the liner to the bin to prevent unauthorised removal; for this, budget locks, pad-locks and various other fixing devices are available.

In some areas, disposable polyethylene bags are being used as liners, but unless the bin is specifically designed to accept and completely contain these liners, their use should be discouraged. Polyethylene bags flapping out of the top of litter bins do nothing to enhance the environment.

The British Standard for litter bins (see chapter 20) specifies four bright colours: red, orange, yellow and blue as well as black, white and grey.

Type C cylindrical locking bin – closed
moulded glass reinforced cement or plastic body and base

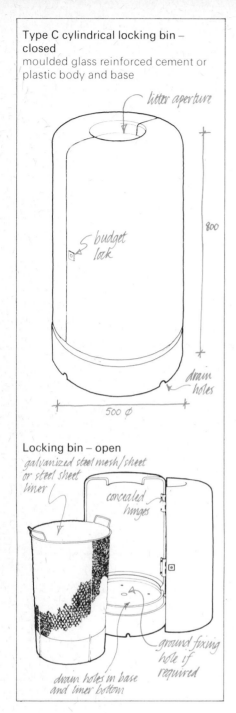

litter aperture

budget lock

800

drain holes

500 ∅

Locking bin – open
galvanized steel mesh/sheet or steel sheet liner

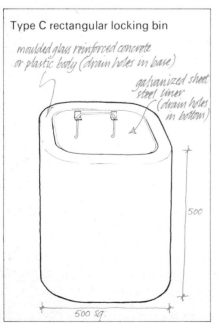

concealed hinges

ground fixing hole if required

drain holes in base and liner bottom

Type C rectangular locking bin
moulded glass reinforced concrete or plastic body (drain holes in base)

galvanized sheet steel liner (drain holes in bottom)

500

500 sq.

Elephant litter bin

body: glass reinforced cement, plastic or galvanized sheet steel

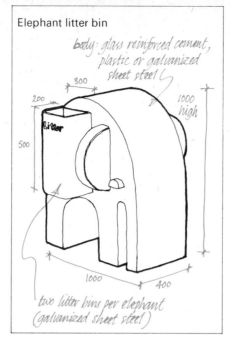

300
200
1000 high
500
Litter

1000
400

two litter bins per elephant (galvanized sheet steel)

Type D rectangular litter bin
this size bin requires two separate liners

glass reinforced cement/plastic body (drain holes in base)

slide away handle

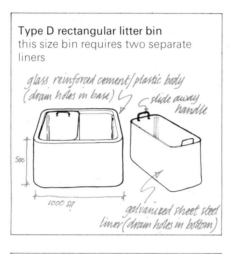

500

1000 sq.

galvanized sheet steel liner (drain holes in bottom)

Type A and B rectangular post or wall mounted litter bin
swivel to empty

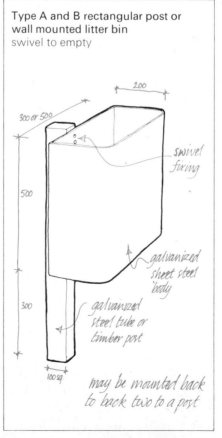

200
300 or 500

swivel fixing

500

galvanized sheet steel body

300

galvanized steel tube or timber post

100 sq

may be mounted back to back two to a post

The colour of the bin should be selected with a view to its state after having been in use for a few months. A brightly painted litter bin, in a comparatively short time, can be a sorry object indeed. Dark and neutral colours tend to resist staining and abuse better than bright colours but are less prominent visually.

Providing litter bins is only the beginning of a continuous chain of events: people being encouraged to drop their litter into bins, emptying bins, carting away litter and very important, the maintenance of bins; well maintained bins, in turn, encourage people to use litter bins. The frequency with which bins are emptied and the money available for maintenance should be carefully considered when the type of bin is being selected. It is usually better to provide a relatively expensive but maintenance free bin than a cheaper bin which requires frequent maintenance or replacement.

The size of bins and the frequency with which they are sited should relate to the number of people in an area, and if the area is subject to seasonal fluctuations, for example, tourist areas and seaside towns, enough bins should be provided to cater for the maximum demand.

As a simple rule of thumb; in busy urban environments, from any one point, one should always be able to see at least two litter bins. They should be geometrically simple in shape having no ostentatious facets or tapers and their colour and finish should be sympathetic to their surroundings, so as not to add to the general clutter.

Useful names (for addresses see chapter 21)
Abacus Municipal Ltd
Barlow, Tyrie Ltd
BFT (Holloware) Co Ltd
Bowater Industrial Packaging Ltd
Braby Group Ltd
British Rail Engineering Ltd
Burnham Signs Ltd
Burnham & Co (Onyx) Ltd
Furnitubes International Ltd
Glasdon Ltd
Greater London Council
A E Griffiths (Smethwick) Ltd
Harvey Fabrication Ltd
Henry Hargreaves & Sons Ltd
R A Lister Farm Equipment Ltd
Metalliform Ltd
Mono Concrete Ltd
Neptune Concrete Ltd
Orchard Seating Ltd
Roto Plastic Containers Ltd
SMP (Landscapes) Ltd
Townscape Products Ltd
Wybone Industrial Sales Ltd
Charles Wicksteed & Co Ltd

16.2 Sand, salt and grit bins

There is often the need to store relatively large volumes of sand, salt and grit, for spreading on footpaths and pavements in icy weather. In some areas street sweepings need to be temporarily stored until they can be collected by lorries for disposal and so on.

Large capacity bins are provided for such needs, the internal volumes ranging from 0.17 m³ (6 ft³) to 1.01 m³ (36 ft³).

These bins should be constructed from materials resistant to corrosion and which require no maintenance, for example; glass reinforced plastics, glass reinforced cement or low density polyethylene.

As the contents of a full bin can be very heavy, 0.17 m³ of grit/salt weighs 230 kilos (4.5 cwt) and 1.01 m³ of gritsalt weights 1323 kilos (26 cwt), it is advantageous if the bins themselves are as light as possible, whilst still being strong enough to withstand possible rough use and abuse.

The bins are usually filled from the top, and emptied with a shovel from the same aperture. A lid should be provided to protect the contents from the weather and it is advisable for this lid to be hinged.

The bins should be sited where they are most needed; sloping footpaths, steps and other hazardous locations, but they should not cause undue obstruction.

A neutral grey, close to the colour of road splash dirt is a sensible choice of colour; unless the bin has a specific use, bright red for fire sand for example. Lettering is often moulded into the lids of the bins to identify the contents.

Useful names (for addresses see chapter 21)
Glasdon Ltd
A E Griffiths (Smethwick) Ltd
Wybone Industrial Sales Ltd

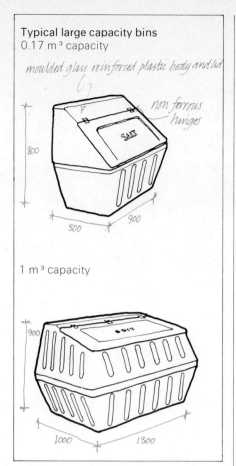

Typical large capacity bins
0.17 m³ capacity

moulded glass reinforced plastic body and lid

non ferrous hinges

SALT

800

500   900

1 m³ capacity

900

1000   1300

16.3 Planters

Planters are containers for top soil in which vegetation may be grown.

They may be permanent or temporary.

Permanent planters are usually built from building materials: natural stone, brick, concrete blocks and insitu concrete.

Temporary unit planters are most commonly made from precast concrete, glass reinforced cement and glass reinforced plastic though the latter is susceptible to vandalism and should not be used except in areas having constant supervision and good security.

Planters make excellent vehicle/pedestrian barriers and the plants they contain can form a useful screen as well as providing colour and oxygen!

Unit planters are frequently used to demarcate experimental pedestrian schemes, where they may have to be removed at twenty four hours notice or even moved about almost on a daily basis. In such instances it is best if the planters are white, to aid driver visibility.

Permanent planters can be built to follow the contour of roads and changes in levels. They can be built to any height, though it is rare to find planters more than 800 mm high. Care must be taken in siting to ensure that drivers sight lines are not interrupted and that necessary access is provided for emergency vehicles.

For plants to be successful they must be regularly watered and the best results are obtained when planters have some form of automatic watering built in. If the cost of this is prohibitive, a hydrant or standpipe (see 3.3) should be provided within hose pipe reach of any planting. Failing this, the services of a water-wagon should be arranged before any planting is brought to site.

If the planter is made from pervious materials, a moisture barrier such as brushed bitument or polyethylene sheeting should be provided inside the planter.

Planters should have weep holes provided at a suitable level, to prevent ponding and the soil becoming waterlogged. The inside of weep holes should be covered with large impervious material, pebbles etc, to prevent them becoming blocked by top soil. When planters are built on free draining sub soil, weep holes are not necessary.

The finish on unit planters should be maintenance free and smooth enough for any dirt to be washed off with a jet from a hose pipe.

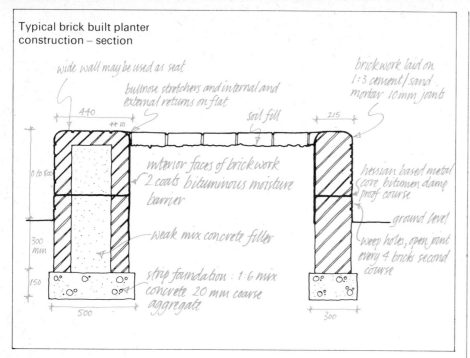

Typical brick built planter
construction – section

wide wall may be used as seat

bullnose stretchers and internal and
external returns on flat

brickwork laid on
1:3 cement/sand
mortar 10mm joints

soil fill

440
±± 10
215

interior faces of brickwork
2 coats bituminous moisture
barrier

0 to 800

hessian based metal
core bitumen damp
proof course

ground level

weak mix concrete filler

300
mm

weep holes, open joint
every 4 bricks second
course

150

strip foundation : 1:6 mix
concrete 20 mm coarse
aggregate

500

300

Planters should be sited so that the
space around them can be easily
cleaned. Any arrangement which might
harbour litter should be avoided.

Once full of soil, unit planters are
exceedingly heavy and can be
impossible to move, so it is important
that the final positions are determined
before they are filled.

Planters are a valuable asset in any
urban environment, whether permanent
or temporary, and their use should be
encouraged whenever and wherever
possible.

In permanent environmental schemes
planters should also be permanent. If an
experimental scheme containing
temporary unit planters becomes
permanent, the temporary planters
should be sited elsewhere and
permanent planters built in their place.

GLC unit planters
moulded glass reinforced cement or
plastic

plan

1000
1000
500
500

drain holes in base

planters may be stacked two high

elevation

500

Useful names (for addresses see
chapter 21.0)
Abacus Municipal Ltd
John Ellis and Sons Ltd
Esplana Ltd
Furnitubes Internatioal Ltd
Glasdon Ltd
Greater London Council
Mono Concrete Ltd
Townscape Products Ltd
Wybone Industrial Sales Ltd

16.4 Seating

It is to be hoped that the environmental
designer will produce areas in which
people might wish to linger and it is
important that seating is provided in
such areas in order that they may be
able to relax in comfort.

Conversely, if the environment is hostile
to pedestrians, such as shopping streets
carrying dense motor traffic, or areas
with high levels of noise and air
pollution (see 4.1), comfortable seats
should **not** be provided to encourage
people to stop and linger.

On the whole, in the urban
environment, there are two distinctly
separate seating needs: long term and
short term.

Long term seating requires
ergonomically designed seats with
backs, where one can sit in comfort for
considerable lengths of time.

Short term seating should be nothing
more elaborate than a simple bench, on
which one can perch for a few minutes.

The Greater London Council has
designed seating made from timber,
galvanised and stainless steel,
aluminium, precast and glass reinforced
concrete, in various combinations.

Short term bench seating can also be
combined with planters and litter bins.

GLC South Bank seating
standard length modules 1 m, 1.5 m,
2 m, 2.5 m, 3 m, (3 m plus as special)

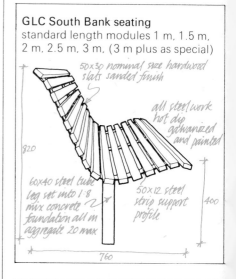

50x30 nominal size hardwood
slats sanded finish

all steelwork
hot dip
galvanized
and painted

820

60x40 steel tube
leg set into 1:8
mix concrete
foundation all in
aggregate 20 max

50x12 steel
strip support
profile

400

760

GLC Thamesmead seating
all steelwork galvanized and painted

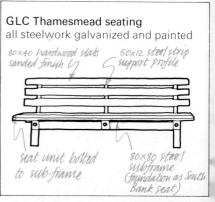

80x40 hardwood slats
sanded finish

50x12 steel strip
support profile

seat unit bolted
to sub-frame

80x80 steel
subframe
(foundation as South
Bank seat)

Short term seating
standard slatted bench

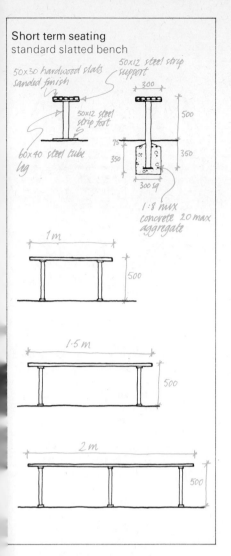

50x30 hardwood slats sanded finish

50x12 steel strip support

300

500

50x12 steel strip foot

60x40 steel tube leg

75

350

350

300 sq

1:8 mix concrete 2.0 max aggregate

1 m
500

1.5 m
500

2 m
500

Standard slats linking planters

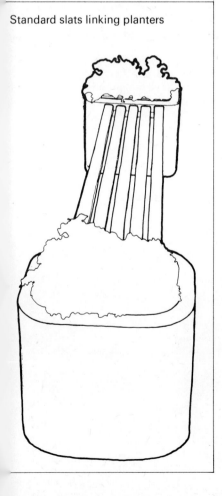

Circular tree seats

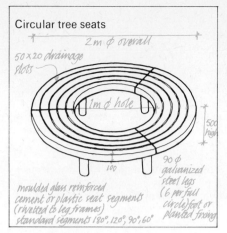

2 m ⌀ overall

50x20 drainage slots

1m ⌀ hole

500 high

100

90 ⌀ galvanized steel legs (6 per full circle) foot or planted fixing

moulded glass reinforced cement or plastic seat segments (riveted to leg frames) standard segments 180°, 120°, 90°, 60°

180° wall mounted tree seat

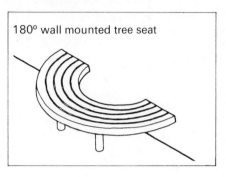

Serpentine seating
standard segments may be combined to form serpentine configurations

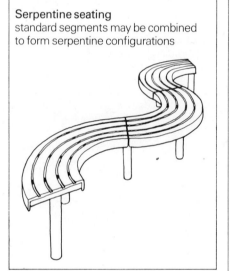

Useful names (for addresses see chapter 21.0)
Abacus Municipal Ltd
Barlow, Tyrie Ltd
British Rail Engineering Ltd
W F Broomfield Ltd
Furnitubes International Ltd
Geometric Furniture Ltd
Glasdon Ltd
Greater London Council
Green Brothers (Geebro) Ltd
Holton Builders Ltd
KUFA Plastics Ltd
S & D Laycock Engineering
Milton Keynes Development Corporation
Mono Concrete Ltd
Neptune Concrete Ltd
Orchard Seating Ltd
Rentaplay Ltd
SMP(Landscapes) Ltd
Townscape Products Ltd
Urban Enviroscape Ltd
VEB Ltd

16.5 Bicycle equipment

As the cost of fuel, and thus transport, is increasing, more and more people are using bicycles as their principle means of transport in towns and cities.

Bicycles are silent, produce no pollution and are ideal vehicles for daily journeys of up to 10 Kilometres or so, particularly if the terrain is relatively flat. Seasoned cyclists, wearing proper apparel, can cycle in all weather conditions other than snow and ice.

Where traffic-free cycle routes are provide (see 5.0 cycletracks), bollards containing the MOT cycle symbol should be used at each entrance, to prevent the ingress of motor vehicles and to identify the route.

GLC cycle track bollard
precast concrete or moulded plastic

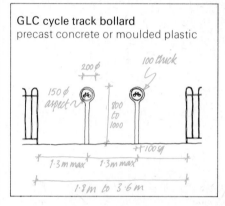

200 ⌀

100 thick

150 ⌀ aspect

800 to 1000

100 sq

1.3 m max

1.3 m max

1.8 m to 3.6 m

As bicyles have become such a desirable means of transport, so the thefts of unattended bicycles have increased and it is necessary to secure a bicycle to an immovable object if it is to be left for any length of time. This is usually accomplished by the use of a lock and chain or similar device, threaded through the cycle frame and wheels, and attached to railings, parking meters, lighting columns, sign supports and so on.

Even though they are legally vehicles, it is a mistake to think of bicycles as small cars which must conform to MOT regulations and have parking spaces allocated to them in the urban environment. Remember that cyclists are nothing more than pedestrians on wheels and as such, should be allowed freedom to ride and park wherever they wish; without of course, endangering or inconveniencing anyone else.

Parking posts should not be provided in public places specifically for the attachment of bicycles, unless there is absolutely nothing else around to which a bicycle may be secured. A cycle post sticking out of the ground at knee height can be very dangerous and inconvenient to pedestrians and is a visual intrusion when not actually holding a bicycle.

In the exceedingly rare event of there being so many bicycles parked in an area as to constitute severe inconvenience to pedestrians, precast concrete parking blocks, which can warp all but the strongest rims, may be set into the ground level with the surrounding surfacing, but as a rule, any token attempt to organise bicycle parking should be discouraged.

16.6 Lifesaving equipment

Wherever there is a high risk of people falling into water and being drowned, such as in the sea, rivers, canals, lakes or reservoirs, lifesaving equipment should be provided.

Where the risk of drowning is extremely high, such as bathing beaches in summer and public swimming pools, lifesaving personnel should be employed, in addition to equipment.

The simplest and most common form of lifesaving equipment is a lifebuoy (also called lifebelt) attached to a length of rope and sited adjacent to the water in a prominent position.

Lifebuoys are available in 600 mm (24 in), 750 mm (30 in) and 900 mm (36 in) diameters, though the latter size is rather too large for most people to throw any distance.

Traditionally, lifebuoys were made from canvas covered cork, but nowadays they are usually made from foam filled pvc or foam filled polyethylene, the ropes being made from rot proof polypropylene roughly 30 m long.

Lifebuoys are most conveniently stored vertically, and may be hung on walls, railings and posts in open or lidded housings. Lidded housings have the advantage of protecting the lifebuoy and rope from the effects of prolonged exposure to the elements. Housings should be as maintenance free as possible, and so plastics have distinct advantages over traditional materials such as painted timber and metal.

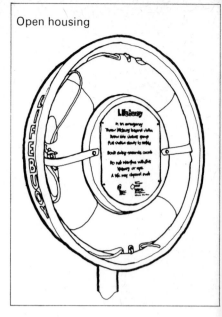

Open housing

A new development in lifebuoy housings has been the inclusion of an alarm which is automatically activated as the lid is lifted off. The alarm consists of a high volume air horn, powered by an air canister which sounds for about 2 minutes continuously.

In addition to summoning attention to an emergency, the alarm is also a very effective anti-vandal device. Dangerous though it may be, lifebuoys are frequently removed by unauthorised persons, and anything which deters them, should be adopted as a matter of course.

As the additional cost of providing an alarm is only 30% of the cost of a standard 600 mm housing and buoy, it is recommended that wherever a lifebuoy is provided, within earshot of people who can alert the emergency services for example, an alarm should be incorporated. This also helps to deter vandals.

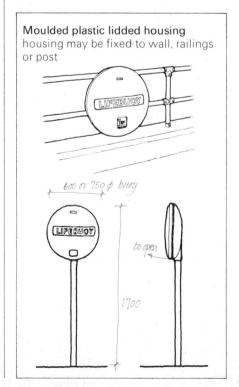

Moulded plastic lidded housing
housing may be fixed to wall, railings or post

LIFEBUOY

600 or 750 ⌀ buoy

LIFEBUOY

to open

1700

Useful names (for addresses see chapter 21)
Charcon Products Ltd
George Fischer Sales Ltd
Greater London Council
Mono Concrete Ltd
Redland Precast Ltd

Useful names (for addresses see chapter 21)
Glasdon Ltd
Perry R & Co Ltd

16.7 Flagpoles

Flagpoles, flags and banners afford a cheap and simple means of bringing colour and interest into virtually any area.

Flags can be useful and decorative. Companies often incorporate their names and logo on flags which they fly at their offices, works and sales outlets.

Flags are usually made from bunting in a mixture of nylon and wool. Depending on the climate and wind speeds, flags will reach a stage where they become so tattered and torn that they have to be replaced. This period can be extended considerably by taking down flags during the hours of darkness and when the wind speed is likely to exceed a force 8 gale. As flags are relatively inexpensive it is often practical to have one or more in reserve.

Flagpoles, traditionally made from timber, are now, more often than not, made from anodised aluminium. They can be wall mounted or free standing.

Typical flagpole and flag

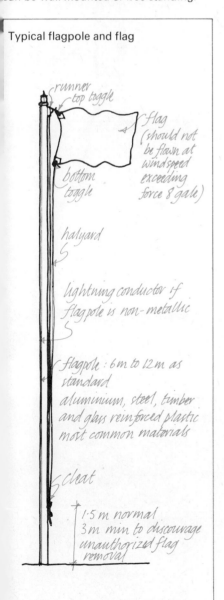

runner
top toggle
flag (should not be flown at windspeed exceeding force 8 gale)
bottom toggle
halyard
lightning conductor if flagpole is non-metallic
flagpole : 6m to 12m as standard
aluminium, steel, timber and glass reinforced plastic most common materials
cleat
1·5 m normal
3m min to discourage unauthorized flag removal

Wall mounted flag poles

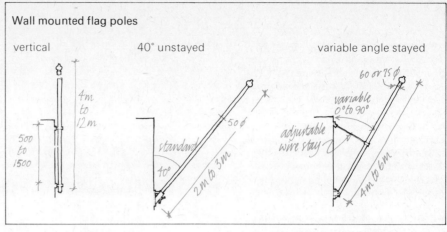

vertical — 4m to 12m, 500 to 1500

40° unstayed — standard 40°, 50 ∅, 2m to 3m

variable angle stayed — 60 or 75 ∅, variable 0° to 90°, adjustable wire stay, 4m to 6m

Freestanding flagpole mountings

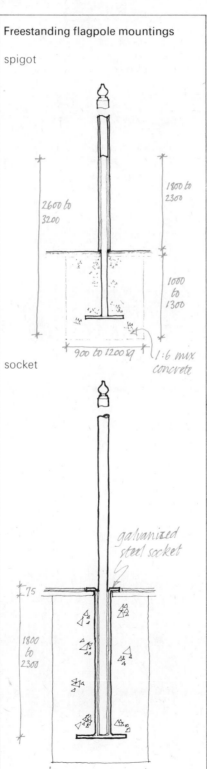

spigot — 2600 to 3200, 1800 to 2300, 1000 to 1300, 900 to 1200 sq, 1:6 mix concrete

socket — galvanized steel socket, 75, 1800 to 2300, 900 to 1200 sq

Surface mounted tabernacle

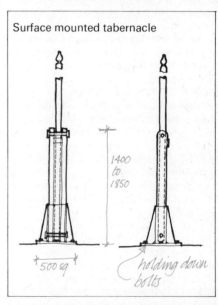

1400 to 1850, 500 sq, holding down bolts

Planted tabernacle

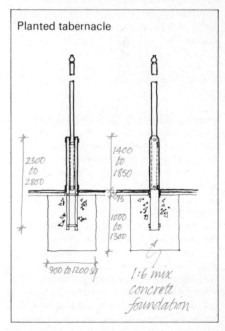

2300 to 2800, 1400 to 1850, 75, 1000 to 1300, 900 to 1200 sq, 1:6 mix concrete foundation

Useful names (for addresses see chapter 21)
Benjamin Edgington Ltd
(Black & Edgington)
Ensign Flag Co Ltd
Non-Corrosive Metal Products Ltd
(Street Furniture Ltd)
Piggott Brothers & Co Ltd

16.8 Clocks

Public clocks are very useful and attractive items to provide in the urban environment, especially in areas which do not already have a means of telling people the time.

Traditionally they are provided as demonstrations of prestige; on town halls, churches, large houses, inns and so on, and for the special needs of travellers, in railway and bus stations, airports and harbours.

Clocks can also be used as advertising devices by carrying the trade names and symbols of shops, companies and so on.

A circular clock can be a very striking feature in an area and often is useful, not only to tell the time by, but as a landmark, focal point and feature.

The fashion towards digital readouts for public clocks should not preclude the use of the traditional face with two or three hands. It has been found that children brought up with digital clocks and watches have little understanding or concept of time, and are unable to tell the time with a traditional clock or watch.

Showpiece clocks are those which provide entertainment in addition to telling the time, the clock on the façade of Fortnum & Mason's in Piccadilly, London, being a particularly fine example of this type. People journey from far and wide to see such spectacles and with the advent of miniature electric motors and modern mechanics it should be easy to design showpiece clocks today. The environmental designer should be aware of the possibility of persuading industry and commerce to invest in show-piece clocks and encourage the provision of such clocks.

For those of more modest means, large faced clocks can be driven by very small electrical movements and so are relatively cheap and simple to install and maintain.

The owners of existing public clocks which no longer work, should be approached by the environmental designer with a view to facilitating the repair or restoration of such clocks.

Local authorities should also be persuaded to provide clocks as a public service, although with rising costs it is doubtful that they will provide showpiece clocks, formerly the common practice on town and county halls.

Clocks can be supported in numerous ways. They can have special freestanding towers built for them, one of the most notable being that of the Houses of Parliament, London containing the famous hour bell 'Big Ben'. They can be housed in small

A rather well known tower clock

Victorian tower clock
about 9 m high

Bracket clock
about 1 m dia face

towers or cupolas on buildings, usually on the roof so that the clock can be seen from all quarters. They can be incorporated into the façade or structure of buildings, be cantilevered out on brackets, hung down on wires, fixed on top of poles and so on. There are all kinds of ingenious ways that can be used to display a clock face at a height suitable for it to be read by the general public, a particularly notable example being a clock set into the pavement, under a toughened glass slab, outside a watchmaker's shop in Windsor High Street, England.

In short, clocks are friendly and bring a sense of identity to an area, and their provision should be encouraged by the environmental designer.

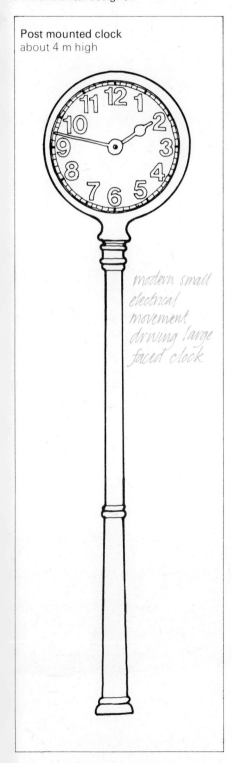

Post mounted clock
about 4 m high

modern small
electrical
movement
driving large
faced clock

Useful names (for addresses see chapter 21)
English Clocks Ltd
(Smiths Industries Ltd)
Gent & Co Ltd

17 Play spaces

Children need challenge and ways to test their imagination, bravery and skill, as a part of their development. This all occurs naturally in the rural environment but in urban surroundings it is very rare indeed to find places where this need can be fulfilled.

Designed urban play spaces are often small hard-surfaced areas, containing one or more items of play equipment, badly designed, manufactured, sited, installed, inspected and maintained. Recently a more welcome trend has been towards adventure playgrounds containing large scale equipment generally designed, constructed and assembled by the children themselves, under the supervision and guidance of adult play leaders.

Housing estates should contain play spaces. Where these do exist they all too often consist of small areas containing nothing more than a few items of play equipment suitable for small children. If any concession is made to the needs of older children it usually appears in the form of a rectangular hard surfaced 'kickabout' area surrounded by chain link fencing about 3m high. These 'kickabout' areas often do not have a wall against which ball games may be played. One or more walls, at least 2m high, are absolutely essential in every 'kickabout' area.

Playground safety has recently become an issue, strongly promoted by the Greater London Council, the Design Council, the Department of Education and Science, the Department of the Environment and numerous other bodies. Many papers and recommendations are readily available and the British Standards Institution has just published two parts of a three part standard dealing with play equipment intended for permanent installation outdoors.

This concern for safety, both in the design of equipment and its siting, has highlighted the major problems associated with typical playgrounds namely; badly designed, manufactured, sited and installed equipment suffering from a lack of regular inspection and maintenance. Hard surfaces under play equipment are also responsible for many injuries to children: for soft surfaces see .1 and 1.2.

However, over-emphasis on safe equipment, lack of vertical drops and restricted layouts, may well be a good way to drive imaginative children to play in hazardous locations such as railway embankments, derelict houses and factories, building sites and so on. Whilst playgrounds containing traditional play equipment should, of course, be as safe as possible, more effort and imagination should be spent

in designing alternative types of playgrounds which do not require maintenance and supervision but give children what they really want.

It is becoming increasingly common, in Scandinavia and Europe, to design natural playgrounds, which are virtually areas of woodland, almost maintenance free and requiring no supervision, except that of parents for very small children. Bernard Lassus; a French environmental designer is a great protagonist of such playgrounds.

In urban England, ecological parks are the nearest things we have to natural playgrounds, but children are certainly not encouraged to play in these.

One has to move out into the suburbs of towns and cities before natural woodland environments can be found where children may play. Wimbledon Common, London is a good example of this, even though London enjoys a fortunate distinction in having so many parks, gardens and open spaces in the central area. There is no good reason why natural playgrounds cannot become a part of every urban park, housing estate, or anywhere, that children need to test their imagination, skill and bravado.

In times of austerity, money is just not available for the supervision, inspection and maintenance of traditional playareas. Natural playgrounds become a much more feasible and cost effective way of providing children with areas for play, recreation and self expression which they so badly need in the urban environment.

In new building sites; housing estates and schools for example, natural playground areas should be set aside during the early stages of the site works. These can then be planted with semi mature trees, bushes, grass and so on and protected whilst building work is being carried out. In this way, the playground will become well established and able to take care of itself, before the buildings are handed over and occupied.

In existing parks and school grounds, areas can be set aside and left to their own devices. Nature will quickly take over and transform these areas into natural playgrounds. In existing housing estates it may be more difficult to establish natural playgrounds and it is vital to obtain the assistance and the co-operation of the children who live on these estates. One way of achieving this is for the children to pay a nominal sum towards the planting of a tree in their name and to actually plant it. In this way, they develop a real awareness of responsibility and care, not only for their own tree but all the others too, and a sense of community in this new natural environment is quickly established.

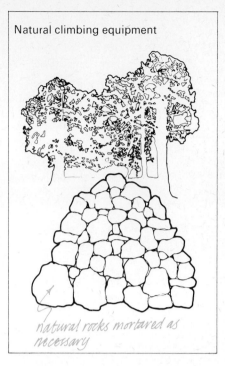

Natural climbing equipment

natural rocks mortared as necessary

If there is absolutely no alternative but to use play equipment in a traditional type of play area, the following manufacturers produce a vast range of equipment from which a choice can be made. Some of this equipment is not approved by some authorities, particularly items with moving parts. The Design Council and other relevant experts should be consulted before equipment, which might constitute an element of danger, is used.

Useful names (for addresses see chapter 21)
Francis Carr
E P Plastics Ltd
Euracel Ltd
Furnitubes International Ltd
Marley Play
Nature—*rocks, slopes, ponds, grass, trees, bushes etc*
Neptune Concrete Ltd
Recticel Ltd
SMP (Landscapes) Ltd
Sportsmark (Leisure Products) Ltd
Tyneside Engineering Ltd
Charles Wicksteed & Co Ltd

18.1 Historic buildings and conservation areas

The design and siting of street furniture and the manner in which ground surfaces are treated can have a considerable effect on the settings of historic buildings and the character of Conservation Areas. The special constraints which apply will vary from case to case, some sensitive buildings and areas requiring a more conservative approach than others. The existing design and landscape character will in all cases need to be studied in detail and it may be necessary to undertake historical and site research or obtain specialized advice before final decisions are taken. It is, nevertheless, possible to lay down a number of general guidelines which should be observed in all circumstances.

Maintenance of existing character

As a general rule, pavings (see 4.4 for road marking) and items of hardware, which are themselves of historic interest or otherwise enhance the character of the area in which they are found, should be preserved in situ. It should be noted that where such items are so closely related to statutorily listed historic buildings as to form part of an architectural design or an inseparable part of a complete fabric (for example, lamps attached to a building, patterned sett or cobble pavings in an enclosed court or bollards surrounding a monument) they will, in many cases, be protected with the building itself. In such circumstances it is an offence to remove or alter them without *Listed Building Consent*. Application for consent is made to the local planning authority, who will also be able to advise as to which buildings and objects are included in the statutory lists. Where a local authority is itself carrying out works requiring listed building consent it cannot grant itself consent but must make an application to the Secretary of State for the Environment.

The completeness of an architectural or landscape design or the integrity of an area of well-defined character may have been mutilated in the past. The carrying-out of essential maintenance or improvements may present opportunities for the restoration of missing or misplaced features. Sometimes the nature of the needed restoration will be obvious but a more searching inquiry may sometimes be needed to establish what originally existed.

Function and siting of re-used old furniture

Older items of street furniture are often

above
Some items of furniture are so completely integrated with an architectural design as to form part of it. In this statutorily listed arcade by John Nash, neither the original iron lamp carriers nor the later gas lanterns can be altered without listed building consent. The appearance of the arcade has suffered by the loss of its original paving and the substitution of a modern jointless surface. The mechanical revolving sign is an unattractive replacement for a traditional barber's pole, which could have been an interesting incident in this view.

left
A bollard designed to protect the corner of a footway from being mounted by carts. The siting of a piece of furniture of this kind is determined by its function. In any other position, its shape would have no meaning.

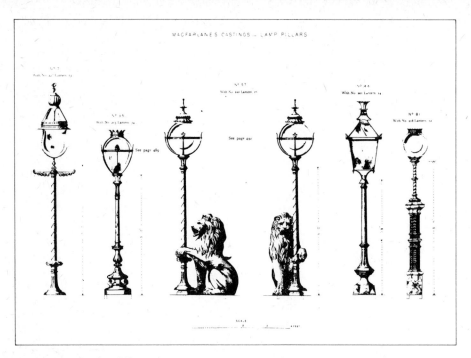

above and above left
Where particularly fine pieces of
furniture have been inherited from the
past, consideration should be given to
restoring even badly damaged items.
The design of the missing lamp standard
and lantern can, in this instance, be
determined by reference to the original
manufacturer's catalogue.

left centre
A London Square; a formal space with
formal furnishings. The layout of the
garden and the design of the enclosing
railings are perfectly integrated with the
surrounding buildings. One axis is
determined by the symmetrical
architectural compositions at the ends,
the other by the approach streets on
either side. Regular lines of bollards
define the edge of the stone-paved
footway and protect if from vehicles on
the more roughly surfaced carriageway.

left below
Area railings, bracket lamps, bollards
and pavings in formal relationship to an
architectural composition.

strikingly ornamented and this can give the mistaken impression that their essential character is ornamental rather than functional. Their deployment as purely decorative 'dressings' to enliven the local scene is, however, rarely defensible. Bollards, spur stones, lamp standards, and other items of furniture have at all periods been designed and sited to serve specific functions and it is important not to rob them of meaning by using them inappropriately.

Even where the original function is obsolete, the historic significance of an object can be enhanced or damaged by its siting. For example, gas lamp standards, even when converted to electricity, look unconvincing if they are too widely or irregularly spaced; a bollard with a swollen base, designed to protect the footway from being mounted by iron-wheeled carts, only makes sense if it is placed on a pavement edge; a public pump must be

in a place where it appears practicable for people in the past to have assembled with cans and buckets and a pavement coal plate must at least appear to serve a basement area vault in front of a building.

Consideration needs to be given not only to the appropriate siting of individual items but also the ways in which whole complexes of furniture are disposed in a historic centre. It is important to distinguish between those cases where the objects contribute to a *formal* character and those where the character to be maintained is *informal*.

The more clearly defined the existing character the more vulnerable it is to inappropriate alterations and additions. The designer may need to submerge his originality and voluntarily limit his range of choice, accepting the constraints imposed by the materials, craft traditions and design forms of the old work.

Formal Spaces

It is particularly important not to confuse an existing *formal* character with informally placed elements of 'foreign' design. Monumentally designed urban spaces are fairly rare in Britain but our older towns contain many examples of squares, circuses, crescents and malls of varying degrees of grandeur, whose regularity and symmetry demand that they be treated in a formal manner. The pavings and furnishings in such spaces are often so discreetly designed and so appropriate to their setting that they are hardly noticed until their formality is damaged or intruded upon. Where, in such a setting, new work is to be closely integrated with the old, it is necessary to observe the letter (and not merely the spirit) of the established design discipline, since the smallest departure tends to draw undue attention to itself.

The illustrations show how the original pavings, bollards, fencing and planting, made important architectural contributions to the character of London squares.

Informal spaces

It is equally important to recognize and safeguard the character of *informal* spaces, whether these are the result of conscious design or of a slow development, guided only by tradition. The small areas of gravel paving which give access to the edge of a village pond, the wooden post and rail fencing guarding vulnerable corners, the spur stones and seemingly casually placed benches and other traditional furnishings on a village green, all contribute to a character which is difficult to create anew, but easily wrecked by the introduction of elements of urban or suburban character. Mass produced kerbing, mechanically spaced and over-tall modern lamp standards, symmetrical flower beds, are especially damaging in this kind of setting. No less damaging is the insensitive attempt to create 'quaint' effects such as self-consciously irregular pavings and

The informal spaces around a village pond call for unselfconscious informal furnishings. The paving, kerbs, simple iron railings, post and rail fences, the culvert arch and the chain barrier, are all completely appropriate in this setting. The sand bin and the street sign (back to camera) are casual additions, but they are reticent enough, at least from this viewpoint, not to be intrusive. The heavy concrete lamp standard with its domed lamp, by contrast, calls attention to itself and its 1950s mannerisms. It is the only object in view whose design shows an agressive attempt to be up-to-date and, as a direct consequence, it is the one object which now looks old-fashioned. As a single jarring note it can fairly easily be overlooked in an otherwise pleasant view, but a regular range of such lamp posts would have a devastating effect on this fragile place.

supposedly 'rustic' timber constructions, which have no foundation in local tradition.

The key to success is the identification of the existing tradition and the drawing up of an extremely limited vocabulary of materials and forms appropriate for use in new work.

New furniture in historic areas

Wherever possible use should be made of good existing furniture in its historical setting and essential replacements and additions should either follow the existing precedents exactly or belong to the same period and 'family' of design. Exact replicas of some of the commonly encountered designs (particularly of iron bollards) can often be obtained from manufacturers, either in the original materials or in a substitute which does not present a disturbing difference of appearance.

top
There can rarely be any objection to a slender lighting standard of unobtrusively traditional design alongside old buildings. Placed, as here, in line with the party wall between two (altered) eighteenth century houses, its presence is hardly noticed. The sign on the right, although smaller, is by contrast, poorly designed and sited in a thoroughly ill-considered way. All that can be said in its favour is that its two messages are on one pole. The street name plate (like the temporary sign and the burglar alarm bell) assumes undue dominance by being placed high up in the middle instead of to one side and it compounds this offence by being slightly off-centre of the centre pier.

above
Measures taken to protect historic areas from traffic intrusion can themselves be damaging. It would be possible to replace these ill-considered assortments of signs and furnishings without loss of effectiveness.

left and left centre
Well-designed Victorian street gates. The directional and other signs needed should be incorporated into a coherent design.

It is sometimes necessary to use modern furniture in conjuction with old. Where there is no historic precedent to be followed for the particular item, the character of existing furniture in the area may nevertheless guide the choice. It should be a primary consideration that the new items should not attract undue attention to themselves by reason of harshly contrasting materials, insubstantial appearance in a setting which calls for robustness, or coarse forms and proportions in a setting which calls for elegance.

above right
The ad hoc appearance of standard industrial furniture like these steel barriers can damage the effect of a considered design.

above and right centre
Interesting pavings can be disfigured by works to Underground Services. Continuing provision needs to be made for the proper reinstatement of pavings after such works. Consultation with statutory undertakers may suggest that disturbance could be minimized by minor changes in the line of new services or modification to the paving pattern.

below left
Cattle troughs have little practical use in towns today but their scarcity value is such that they are often listed by the DoE as being of special architectural or historic interest. Whether plain or elaborate and monumental they can make an irreplaceable contribution to the street scene. Their original function demands that they be sited at the kerbside or in some other position where horses might be watered.

below right
Even where the design of pieces of furniture is not of the highest quality it is often spirited and expresses a kind of civic pride which should be respected. The missing end arm rest of this seat should be replaced.

18.2 Consents and consultations

Listed buildings
For procedure regarding consent to demolish or alter items included in the statutory list of buildings of special architectural, or historic interest: see Maintenance of Existing Character 18.1

Conservation areas
Local planning authorities may have formulated detailed design policies and set up special consultation procedures in conservation areas which they have designated under S.277 of the Town and Country Planning Act 1971.

Once an area is designated, there is a statutory requirement (S.277(8)) that special attention shall be paid to the desirability of preserving or enhancing its character or appearance, and this applies in particular to the exercise of *any* powers under the 1971 Act.

Listed building consent is now (since the Town and Country Amenities Act 1974) required for the demolition of unlisted buildings in a Conservation area. This applies only to buildings and there are a number of exceptions to this form of control (eg buildings not exceeding 115 cubic metres) but the removal of quite small structures, eg shelters and street furniture, can have a harmful effect on the character or appearance of an area. Even where an authority or undertaker is under no statutory obligation to obtain consent for work being executed, the local planning office should be consulted as to its requirements in, or adjoining, Conservation areas.

18.3 'Reproduction' furniture

The recent upsurge of interest in the conservation of areas, has led to a demand for 'reproduction' furniture which faithfully represents what was, or might have been originally on a particular site.

Old photographs and manufacturers' catalogues — the old Macfarlanes catalogue of cast iron goods is a good example – contain much information from which copies can be made of the originals although copies of such attractive books now command fairly high prices. The Historic Buildings Division of The Greater London Council can also sometimes provide useful information.

If an original piece of furniture still survives, then it is a fairly simple process to copy it, though not necessarily in the original materials.

The ornate and historic St. Martins bollards in Leicester Square, London, are a good example of this:

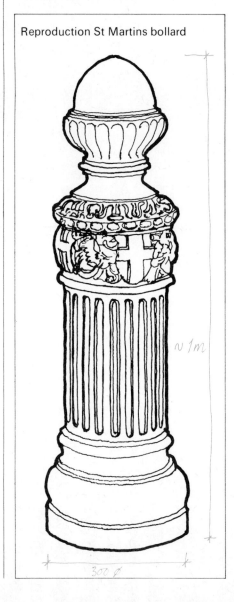

Reproduction St Martins bollard

~ 1m

300 ⌀

Eighty were needed for the new pedestrian scheme, but only four cast iron originals still remained. The best of the four were unearthed and taken to a company of modellers and mould makers – who incidentally make moulds for Henry Moore – for restoration, which involved stripping off at least 10mm of paint, and modelling-in details long since vanished due to corrosion.

A flexible rubber ('vinamould') mould was made from the restored bollard. This mould was then taken to a manufacturer in Yorkshire and the bollards were cast in glass reinforced cement (grc) around a galvanised mild steel support tube. After the curing period the bollards were painted with primer and delivered to site to be erected and painted in the usual way.

A direct comparison was made between copying the bollards in grc or cast iron and as, at the time, the cost of a grc bollard was 25 per cent of that of a cast iron bollard, the choice was not too difficult to make. When painted, the bollards look identical and only someone who knows which is which can spot the difference.

Cast aluminium is also frequently used as a substitute for cast iron.

The most common historic items requested for copying seem to be gas lamps, bench seats, bollards and railings, though anything can be copied given the will, the time and the money.

Such has been the demand, that manufacturers are digging out old patterns and designs and marketing historic seats and lamps etc., as part of their every day ranges. It is interesting that old crafts, such as copper and tin-smithing, are once again being practised.

Cast iron gun barrel bollard

1000

200 ⌀

Cast iron wall mounted lantern

Historic post top fitting

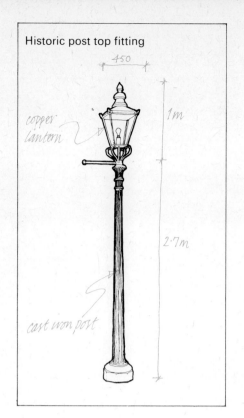

450

copper lantern

1m

2·7m

cast iron post

Traditional seating

cast iron ends and support

hardwood slats

400

lengths: 1830
2440
3050

700

cast iron ends and support

hardwood slats

2440

800

Reproduction pre-Victorian seat

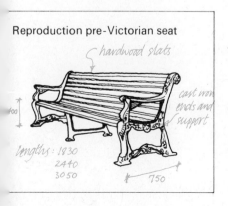

hardwood slats

cast iron ends and support

400

lengths: 1830
2440
3050

750

Useful names (for addresses see chapter 21)
Grahamston Iron Co
Mather & Smith
Norlett Ltd
Norman & Raymond
Phosco Ltd
Sloan & Davidson
D W Windsor Ltd
Wybone Industrial Sales Ltd

19 Co-ordinated street furniture

The urban environment can basically be divided into three distinctly separate areas:

Area 1   Complicated and cluttered areas, which are the largest constituent of most towns and cities.
Area 2   Areas having special historic and architectural quality.
Area 3   Parkland and semi-rural areas.

In a bid to satisfy the needs of each of these areas, the Greater London Council is designing 3 co-ordinated ranges of furniture.

Range 1, for use in area 1 is composed of ultra simple geometric forms which co-ordinate dimensionally and are designed to be as self-effacing as possible.

Range 2 is composed of items which complement area 2. By the use of modern technology and materials, historic furniture can be faithfully reproduced at competitive cost. Items in this range are designed as features and not to be self effacing, but they use some components common to the other ranges.

Range 3 is composed of items which use traditional rural techniques and materials and are designed to be simple and blend with their surroundings.

The ranges largely conform to length/width/diameter modular co-ordinates of 100, 200, 500 and 1000 mm and height co-ordinates of 100, 500, 800, 1000, 1500, 2000 and 2500 mm though lighting columns are 5, 8, 10 and 12 metres high.

All the items are designed to fulfil ergonomic requirements, not only while in use but in handling, installation and maintenance.

The materials selected have a very high resistance to weathering and vandalism, and yet are cost effective and relatively maintenance free. The major materials used are: glass-reinforced cement, pre-cast concrete, timber, metal and plastics, for the mass produced items, but in the range for the historic and architectural areas, natural stone and other expensive materials are used.

All maintenance is capable of being accomplished by the use of basic tools and materials. If areas are well maintained, vandalism and deterioration are appreciably lessened.

The items of which the ranges are comprised, are produced by various different manufacturers selected to give the best value for money, and are available direct from the manufacturers sales departments.

The Greater London Council ranges of street furniture are continuously being re-appraised and updated and wherever a specific need is identified, the ranges are extended to encompass that requirement.

A selection of Greater London Council street furniture

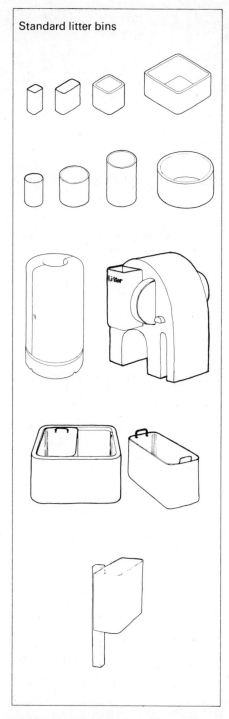

Standard litter bins

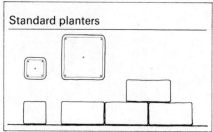

Standard planters

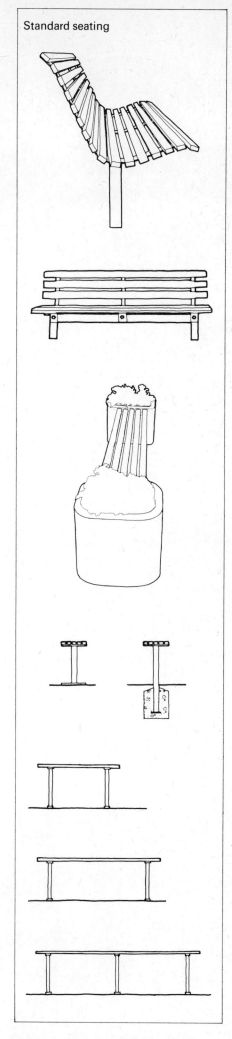

Standard seating

Standard seating

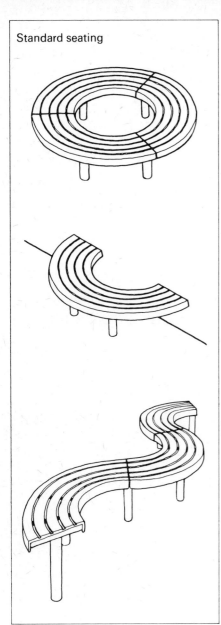

Standard bollards

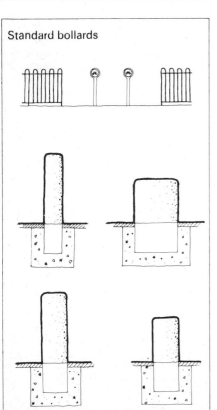

Standard poster boards

Standard road lighting columns

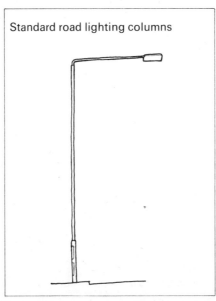

Standard amenity light

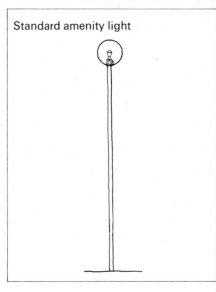

Standard guard railing, fences and gates

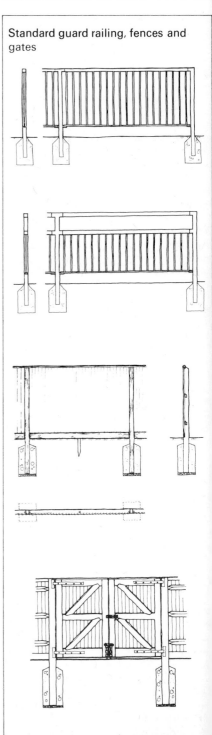

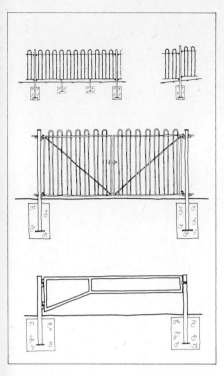

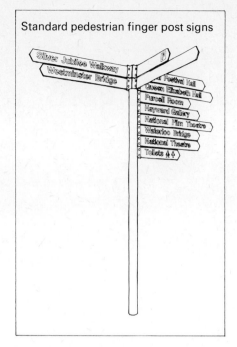

Standard pedestrian finger post signs

Typical gantries

Typical reproduction bollard

Typical traffic direction signs

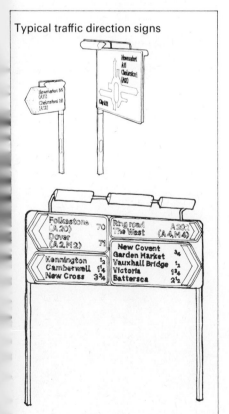

RELEVANT BRITISH STANDARDS

All numbers are BS unless prefixed by:

PD   Public Documents
CP   Codes of Practice
MA   Marine Standards
DD   Drafts for Development
PAS Public Authority Standards

The British Standards Institute publishes four kinds of documents. Most of these are known as British Standards, each with a number and the prefix BS. These Standards include product specifications, test methods, procedural recommendations, glossaries, schedules, conversion tables and other basic data. Also included in this BS group are *new* Codes of Practice (published since around 1975) which are headed BS 0000 Code of Practice for . . . . The CP prefix before the number will remain for some time however, for *old* Codes of Practice, published before about 1975.

CP's are defined as 'recommendations for good practice to be followed during design, manufacture, construction, installation and maintenance, with a view to safety, quality, economy and fitness for purpose.' Most CP's are concerned with the construction industry, although some deal with engineering.

Draft for Development (DD) are issued in lieu of British Standards when firm specifications cannot be laid down either because the subject is too new or because there is not available sufficient information.

Published Document (PD) is the prefix used for publications which do not fall into other categories.

British Standards, CPs, DDs and PDs are available from BSI, 2 Park Street, London W1A 2BS.

In the USA the broad equivalent of BSI is the American National Standards Institute, which publishes a range of standard documents.

masonry	3826
Well casing, for water wells	879
Wood flooring:	
blocks	1187
Wood poles for overhead lines	1990
Wood preservatives:	
classification, application	1282
coal tar	144, 3051
copper/chrome	3452
copper/chrome/arsenic, waterborne	4072
copper naphthenate	5056
creosote	144, 913
Zinc coatings on iron and steel	1706
galvanized	729
— *corrugated sheet*	3083
— *sheet and coil*	2989
— *wire*	443
sheradized	4921
sprayed	2569

Conversion table
Feet and inches (up to 10 ft) to metres and millimetres (to nearest millimetre)

Feet	Inches											
	0	**1**	**2**	**3**	**4**	**5**	**6**	**7**	**8**	**9**	**10**	**11**
	Metres and Millimetres											
0		25	51	76	102	127	152	178	203	229	254	279
1	305	330	356	381	406	432	457	483	508	533	559	584
2	610	635	660	686	711	737	762	787	813	838	864	889
3	914	940	965	991	1·016	1·041	1·067	1·092	1·118	1·143	1·168	1·194
4	1·219	1·245	1·270	1·295	1·321	1·346	1·372	1·397	1·422	1·448	1·473	1·499
5	1·524	1·549	1·575	1·600	1·626	1·651	1·676	1·702	1·727	1·753	1·778	1·803
6	1·829	1·854	1·880	1·905	1·930	1·956	1·981	2·007	2·032	2·057	2·083	2·108
7	2·134	2·159	2·184	2·210	2·235	2·261	2·286	2·311	2·337	2·362	2·388	2·413
8	2·438	2·464	2·489	2·515	2·540	2·565	2·591	2·616	2·642	2·667	2·692	2·718
9	2·743	2·769	2·794	2·819	2·845	2·870	2·896	2·921	2·946	2·972	2·997	3·023
10	3·048	3·073	3·099	3·124	3·150	3·175	3·200	3·226	3·251	3·277	3·302	3·327

USEFUL NAMES AND ADDRESSES

Abacus Municipal Ltd
Sutton-in-Ashfield
Notts NG17 5FT
(0623) 511111

Abru Aluminium Ltd
Building Products Division
Pennygillam Industrial Estate
Launceston,
Cornwall PL15 7ED
(0566) 3535

Adamson Butterley Ltd
Ripley
Derby DE5 3BQ
(0773) 46111

Adshel Ltd
19 Curzon Street
London W1Y 8BJ
01-499 8146

Amerace-Esna Ltd
Chantry Road
Kempston
Bedford MK42 7ST
(0243) 851451

Anglian Building Products Ltd
Atlas Works
Lenwade
Norwich NR9 5SW
(060 544) 291

APT Ltd
Aptcorn House
49–51 Gough Street
London WC1
01-278 1401

ARC Concrete Ltd
Elms Court
West Way
Botley
Oxford OX2 9LR
(0865) 46351

Association of Public Lighting Engineers
78 Buckingham Gate
London SW1E 6PF
01-834 3655

Astolat Co Ltd
Peasmarsh
Guildford
Surrey
(0483) 75211

Atlas Stone Company Ltd
Artillery House
Artillery Row
London SW1P 1RU
01-222 2091

Edward Barber & Co Ltd
Paxton Road
Tottenham
London N17
01-808 5161

Barlow Tyrie Ltd
Springwood Industrial Estate
Rayne Road
Braintree
Essex CM7 7RN
(0376) 22505

Bell & Webster Ltd
Belcon House
Essex Road
Hoddesdon
Herts EN11 0DR
(61) 67141

Berger Traffic Markings Ltd
Berger House
Berkeley Square
London W1X 6NB
01-629 9171

Bergo Ltd
Otterspool Way
Watford WD2 8HY
(0923) 26014

Richard Berry & Son
Birmingham Road
West Bromwich
Staff
(021 553) 1766/8

BFT (Holloware) Co Ltd
10/13 Hill Street
Kidderminster
Worc DY11 6TD
(0562) 4225

Bison (Garages) Ltd
Sandy Lane
Chadwell St Mary
Grays
Essex RM16 4LR
(037 52) 2291

Harold Bloom Signs (Sales) Ltd
36 North End Road
London NW11 7PT
01-455 3482

William Booth and Co (Metal Work) Ltd
Palatine Works
Causeway Avenue
Warrington
Cheshire WA4 6QQ
(0925) 33569

Borer Engineering Co Ltd
Stocks Lane,
Bracklesham Bay
Chichester
West Sussex PO20 8NT
(0243) 670711

Bowater Industrial Packaging Ltd
North Road Industrial Estate
Ellesmere Port
Cheshire L65 1AQ
(051 355) 1951

Braby Group Ltd
Ashton Gate Works
Bristol BS3 2LQ
(0272) 664041

G Brady & Co Ltd
Ilsington Works
Ancoats
Manchester M60 0BL
(061 205) 2797

W H Brady Co Ltd
Daventry Road Industrial Estate
Banbury
Oxfordshire OX16 7JU
(0295) 56101

Bribex Ltd
The Croft
Yate
Bristol BS17 5QN
(045) 424440

Bribond Signs Ltd
Burgess Hill
Sussex
(04446) 5611

Brick Advisory Centre
26 Store Street
London WC1E 7BT
01-637 0047

The Brick Development Association
Woodside House
Winkfield
Windsor SL4 2DP
(034 47) 5651

Brickhouse Dudley Ltd
Dudley Road West
Tipton
West Midlands DY4 7XD
(021 557) 3922

British Aluminium Building Products Ltd
Norfolk House
St James's Square
London SW1Y 4JS
01-839 8888

British Aluminium Co Ltd
Regal House
London Road
Twickenham TW1 3QA
01-892 4488

British Dredging (Concrete Products) Ltd
Corporation Road
Newport
Gwent NPT 0WT
(0633) 71204

British Rail Engineering Ltd
Railway Technical Centre
London Road
Derby DE2 8UP
(0332) 49211

British Standards Institution
2 Park Street
London W1A 2BS
01-629 9000
(Sales)
101 Pentonville Road
London N1
01-837 8801

British Steel Corporation, Tubes Division
Structural Design Centre
Corby Works
Corby
Northants NN17 1UA
(053 66) 2121

Broads Manufacturing Co Ltd
Western Road
Bracknell
Berks
(0344) 24545

Brockhouse Berry Ltd
Birmingham Road
West Midlands B71 4JP
(021 553) 1766

Brooklyns Westbrick Ltd
1 Market Close
Poole
Dorset BH15 1NH
(020 13) 5751

W F Broomfield Ltd
The Old Bakehouse
Ward Road
Totland Bay,
Isle of Wight PO39 0BB
(098 383) 2921

Buffalo Fence Ltd
19 Mill Lane
Benson,
Oxford OX9 6SA
(0491) 38368

**Burgess Architectural Products
Ltd**
Brookfield Road
Hinckley
Leicestershire LE10 2LN
(0455) 37701/35579

Burnham Signs
Burnham and Co (Onyx) Ltd
Kangley Bridge Road
Lower Sydenham
London SE26 5AL
01-659 1525

Burt Boulton (Timber) Ltd
Brettenham House
Lancaster Place
London WC2E 7EN
01-836 5801

Butterley Building Materials Ltd
Wellington Street
Ripley
Derby DE5 3DZ
(0773) 43661

Francis Carr
2 Christ Church Road
London N8 9QL
01-340 6740

C-Cure Coatings Ltd
Woodilee Industrial Estate
Kirkintilloch
Glasgow
Scotland G66 3UR
(041 776) 5480

Cement and Concrete Association
Wexham Springs
Slough
Bucks SL3 6PL
(028 16) 2727

Charcon Products Ltd
Hulland Ward
Derby DE6 3ET
(0332) 31262

C M Churchouse Ltd
Lichfield Road
Brownhills
Staffs WS8 6LA
(054 33) 3551

City Guides Ltd
Dudley Road
Tunbridge Wells
Kent
(0892) 24575

Civic Trust
17 Carlton House Terrace
London SW1Y 5AW
01-930 0914

Claudgen Traffic Signs
Wembley Hill Estate
Wembley
Middlesex
01-902 3682

Cohen Brothers (Electrical) Ltd
Tetlow Bridge Engineering Works
Crumpsall
Manchester M8 6XB
(061 740) 1303

Colorguard Ltd
Dennis Road
Tan House Industrial Estate
Widnes
Lancs WA8 0SH
(051) 424 6741

Concentric (Fabrications) Ltd
52/56 Standard Road
Park Royal
London NW10 6HH
01-965 2941

Concrete (Northern Ireland) Ltd
Langford Lodge
53 Largy Road
Crumlin
Co Antrim
Northern Ireland
(02384) 52328

Concrete Utilities Ltd
Great Amwell
Ware
Herts SG12 9TA
(0920) 2272/6

Control Systems Ltd
The Island
Uxbridge
Middlesex UB8 2UT
(89) 51255

**Albert Cook and Son (Founders)
Ltd**
Wincolmlee
Hull
Yorks HU2 0QF
(0482) 20099

Deans Blinds
13 Deodar Road
Putney
London SW15 2NR
01-789 0121

Department of the Environment
2 Marsham Street
London SW1P 3EB
01-212 3434

**Dorman Smith Traffic Products
Ltd**
Cambridge Park Estate
Southport PR9 9YF
(0704) 20911

Dunlop Ltd
Dunlop House
Ryder Street
London SW1Y 6RA
01-930 6700

Du Pont (UK) Ltd
Maylands Avenue
Hemel Hempstead
Herts
(0442) 61251

Durafencing Ltd
9 Motcomb Street
London SW1
01-235 8122

Dymo Ltd
Pier Road
Feltham
Middlesex TW14 0TR
01-890 1388

Benjamin Edgington Ltd
Ruxley Corner
Sidcup
Kent DA14 5AQ
01-302 2525

Eleco Ltd
Campfield Road
St Albans
Herts AL1 5HU
(56) 54524

E J Elgood Ltd
Insulcrete Works
Yeoman Street
London SE8 5DU
01-237 1144

Electromatic Sunblinds Ltd
201 Eade Road
Finsbury Park
London N4 1RA
01-800 6617

John Ellis and Sons Ltd
Sileby Road
Barrow-on-Soar
Loughborough
Leicestershire
(050 981) 2601

English Clocks Ltd
(Smiths Industries Ltd)
8 Chase Road
Park Royal
London NW10
01-965 9011

English Tourist Board
4 Grosvenor Gardens
SW1W 0DU
01-730 3400

Ensign Flag Co Ltd
66/68 Kitchen Street
Liverpool L1 0AN
(051 709) 1845

EP Plastics Ltd
152 Newport Street
London SE11 6AQ
01-582 8660

Esplana Ltd
49 Masons Hill
Bromley
Kent BR2 9HP
01-460 2003

Eternit Building Products Ltd
Whaddon Road
Meldreth
Royston
Herts SG8 5RL
(0763) 60421

Euracel Ltd
Commerce Estate
Kingston Road
Leatherhead
Surrey KT22 7LA
(53) 76334

EVB Engineering Ltd
Seager Place
Burdett Road
London E3
01-980 2571

Expamet Contracts Ltd
PO Box 130
Ashburton Grove
London N7
01-607 6332

Fabrikat Engineering Co Ltd
Fabenco Works
Urban Road
Kirkby in Ashfield
Nottingham NG17 8AP
(0623) 752681

Factuweld Ltd
Chewton Street
Eastwood
Notts NG16 3JN
(077 37) 66765

Fairway Tehnical Plastics Ltd
Battersea Road
Heaton Mersey Industrial Estate
Stockport
Cheshire SK4 3EP
(061 432) 1885

Field Engineering
A division of Field Aircraft Services
Wymeswold Aerodrome
Burton on the Wold
Nr Loughborough
Leics LE12 5TR
(0509) 880133

Finalite Co Ltd
Water Lane Trading Estate
Storrington
Sussex RH20 3DT
(090 66) 3245/6/7

George Fischer Sales Ltd
Eagle Wharf Road
London N1 7EE
01-253 1044

Fisher-Karpark Ltd
Gratrix Works
Sowerby Bridge
West Yorkshire HX6 2PH
(0422) 33533

Fleet Markings Ltd
Queensway Industrial Estate
Wrexham
Clwyd LL13 8YR
(0978) 55283

Florastone British Uralite Ltd
Higham
Rochester
Kent ME3 7JA
(047 482) 3451

Forest City Electric Co Ltd
4 Longford Road
Stretford
Manchester M32 0HS
(061 865) 2475

Forest City Signs Ltd
Park Road
Timperley
Altrincham
Cheshire WA14 5QX
(061 969) 0441

Franco Signs Ltd
Aerodrome Road
Colindale
London NW9
01-205 6581

Furnitubes International Ltd
90 Royal Hill
Greenwich
London SE10 8RT
01-691 0019/0

GEC Ltd
PO Box 17
East Lane
Wembley
Middlesex HA9 7PG
01-904 4321

Gent & Co Ltd
Faraday Works
Leicester LE5 4J4
(0533) 730251

Geometric Furniture Ltd
The Old Mill
Shepherd Street
Royton
Oldham
Lancs OL2 5PB
(061) 633 1119

Glasdon Ltd
117-123 Talbot Road
Blackpool
Lancs FY1 3QY
(0253) 22378/9

Glynwed Tubes & Structures Ltd
Queensgate Works
Bilston Road
Wolverhampton WV2 2NJ
(0902) 21633

Godwin Warren Eng Ltd
Emery Road
Bristol BS4 5PW
(0272) 778399

Goodlas Wall & Co Ltd
Ibex House
Minories
London EC3
01-488 3536/7

Grahamston Iron Co
PO Box 5
Falkirk
Stirlingshire
Scotland
(0324) 22661

The Greater London Council
The County Hall
London SE1 7PB
01-633 5000

Green Brothers (Geebro) Ltd
(Lister Woodcraft Divison)
Hailsham
East Sussex
(0323) 840771

A E Griffiths (Smethwick) Ltd
Booth Street
Smethwick
Warley
West Midlands B66 2PE
(021 558) 1571/1558

Gydelite Ltd
Beacon House
Beacon Way
Banstead
Surrey
(25) 55077

Haldo Developments Ltd
The Fort
Bury St Edmunds
Suffolk IP33 2BN
(0284) 4043

Hale & Hale Engineers Ltd
Upper Church Lane
Tiptree
Staffs 9Y4 8N2
(021 557) 3446

Henry Hargreaves and Sons Ltd
Lord Street
Bury
Lancs BL9 0RG
(061 764) 5082

T A Harris Ltd
134 New Kent Road
London SE1 6TY
01-703 3842/3

Harvey Fabrication Ltd
Woolwich Road
Charlton
London SE7 7RJ
01-858 3232

Hawesigns Ltd
Beresford Avenue
Wembley
Middlesex HA0 1RX
01-903 3181/5

Hawkins Tiles (Cannock) Ltd
Longhouse Works
Watling Street
Cannock
Staffordshire
(054 35) 3744

Healey John (London) Ltd
32 Shaftesbury Avenue
London W1V 7DD
01-437 2610

Highway Equipment Manufacturing Co Ltd
Debdale Lane
Mansfield Woodhouse
Notts NG19 9NR
(0623) 29231/2

Hills Patents Ltd
Hills House
London Road
Staines
Middlesex
(81) 4471/5

Holophane Europe Ltd
Bond Avenue
Bletchley
Milton Keynes MK1 1JG
(0908) 74661

Holton Furniture
Holton cum Beckering
Wragby
Lincoln LN3 5NG
(067 34) 348

Ibstock Building Products Ltd
Ibstock
Leicester LE6 1HS
(0530) 60531

IG Engineering Co Ltd
Avondale Road
Cwmbran
Gwent NP4 1XY
(063 33) 66811

Iudex Ltd
The Manor
East Haddon
Northampton NN6 8BU
(060 125) 365

Jardine (Leisure Furniture) Ltd
PO Box 32B
East Molesey
Surrey KT8 9SP
01-979 6668

J A King (Glascrete) Ltd
Disraeli Road
Harlesden
London NW10 7BT
01-965 8937

KUFA Plastics Ltd
2 Lyon Close
Chantry Estate
Kempston
Bedford MK42 7SB
(0234) 854464

Laird (Anglesey) Ltd
Beaumaris
Gwynedd
North Wales LL58 8HY
(024 883) 431

S & D Laycock Engineering Ltd
Swinnow Lane
Stanningley
Pudsey
West Yorkshire LS28 7XE
(0532) 578141

Lighting Design & Manufacturing Services (Essex) Ltd
28 Gaynesford
Basildon
Essex
(0268) 43581

Lindvale Plastics Ltd
Waverley Street
Coatbridge
Lanarkshire
Scotland
(0236) 26181/2

R A Lister Farm Equipment Ltd
Dursley,
Gloucestershire GL11 4HS
(0453) 2371

London and Provincial Posters Ltd
78/86 Brigstock Road
Thornton Heath
Surrey CR4 7JA
01-689 2131

Luminor Ltd
Enfield Chase Depot
Windmill Hill
Enfield
Middlesex
01-363 4389

Lumitron Ltd
Chandos Road
London NW10 6PA
01-965 0211

Luxcrete Ltd
Disraeli Road
Harlesden
London NW10 7BT
01-965 7292

3M Company Ltd
Wigmore Street
PO Box 1ET
London W1A 1ET
01-486 5522

Marley Buildings Ltd
Guildford
Surrey GU3 1LS
(0483) 69922

Marley Play
Chantry Lane
Storrington
Sussex RH20 4AD
(090 66) 3221

Marryat & Scott Ltd
Wellington Works
Hounslow
London TW4 5JN
01-570 7799

S Marshall & Sons Ltd
Southowram
Halifax
Yorks HX3 9SY
(0422) 22201

Mather & Smith
General Iron Founders
Brunswick Road
Ashford
Kent TN23 1ED
(0233) 24911

A W May Ltd
1 Clements Road
East Ham
London E6 2DT
01-472 0078

Mendip Stone and Concrete Co Ltd
Leigh on Mendip
Bath
Somerset BA3 5QF
(037 381) 396

Merchant Adventures Ltd
Interlight House
Hampton Road West
Feltham
Middlesex TW13 6DR
01-894 5522

Metalliform Ltd
Platts Common
Industrial Estate
Hoyland
Barnsley
South Yorkshire S74 0EZ
(0226) 742187

Metalline Graphics Ltd
Winster Grove
Birmingham B44 9EJ
(021 357) 1753

Mills and Allen Ltd
160 Swan Lane
Coventry CV2 4HD
(0203) 22292

Milton Keynes Development Corporation
Wavendon Tower
Wavendon
Milton Keynes
Bucks MK17 8LX
(0908) 74000

Mitco Blinds
Unit 7
Elizabeth Industrial Estate
New Cross
London SE14 5RR
01-692 7878

Monoconcrete (Holdings) Ltd
Oxclose Lane
Mansfield
Woodhouse
Nottingham
(0623) 25331

Mono Concrete Ltd
Wettern House
Dingwall Road
Croydon CR9 2NY
01- 686 4311

Mor-Line Road Markers Ltd
PO Box 14
Tonbridge
Kent TN10 4HX
(0732) 351274

Trevor Morrison Engineering Ltd
13 Brecknock Road
London N7 0BL
01-485 6915

Natural Stone Directory
Ealing Publications
73a High Street
Maidenhead
Berks SL8 1JX
(0628) 23562

John Needham & Sons Ltd
Portwood Foundry
Carrington Road
Stockport
Cheshire SK1 2JV
(061 480) 4026

Neptune Concrete Ltd
Quayside Road
Bitterne Manor
Southampton SO9 4YP
(0703) 25513

Neolite Ltd
London Road
Wrotham
Sevenoaks
Kent TN1 57TA
(0732) 2256

Thomas Ness Ltd
Cardiff Road
Nantgarw
Cardiff CF4 7YH
(044 385) 2511

**Non-Corrosive Metal Products Ltd
(Street Furniture Ltd)**
Horton Road
West Drayton
Middlesex
(81) 42607

Norlett Ltd
Dormer Road
Thame
Oxfordshire
(084421) 4161

Norman & Raymond
122 Stonhouse Street
Clapham
London SW4 6AL
01-622 4242

Norman and Sons (Marketing) Ltd
12 High Street
Egham
Surrey TW20 9HD
(07843) 7777

The Ockley Brick Co Ltd
Smokejacks Brickworks
Walliswood
Nr Ockley
Surrey
(0306) 79 481/3

Olympiad Signs Ltd
526 High Road
Leytonstone
London E11 3EQ
01-539 3770

Orchard Seating Ltd
Orchard House
St Martin's Street
Wallingford
Oxon OX10 0DE
(0491) 36588

Osram (GEC) Ltd
PO Box 17
East Lane
Wembley
Middlesex HA9 7PG
01-904 4321

Otis Elevator Co Ltd
94/96 Newhall Street
Birmingham 3
(021 236) 4061

L V Pannell Ltd
Duke Street
New Basford
Nottingham NG7 7JN
(0602) 700371

Pearce Gowshall Ltd
Park Lane
Oldbury
Warley
Worcs
(021 552) 2291

Pearce Signs Ltd
Insignia House
New Cross
London SE14 6AB
01-692 6611

**Pearl and Dean (Outdoor
Advertising) Ltd**
Broadwick Street
London W1
01-734 8832

Perma Blinds Ltd
Prospect Row
Dudley
West Midlands DY2 8SE
(0384) 214231

Perry R & Co Ltd
90 Church Street
Birkenhead
Merseyside L41 5EQ
(051 647) 6416

Philips Electrical Ltd
Lighting Division
City House
London Road
Croydon CR9 3QR
01-686 0505

Phosco Ltd
Great Amwell
Ware
Herts SG12 9LR
(0920) 2041

Piggott Brothers & Co Ltd
Standford Rivers
Ongar
Essex
(027 76) 3262

George Pike Ltd
Equipment Works
Alma Street
Birmingham 6
(021 359) 2101

PJP Trading Ltd
Queensway House
Queensway
Hatfield
Herts AL10 0NP
(30) 66726

Plastic Coatings Ltd
Trading Estate
Farnham
Surrey
(025 13) 4981

The Plessey Co Ltd
Electronics Group
Automation Division
Sopers Lane
Poole
Dorset
(02013) 5161

Portakabin Ltd
Huntington
York YO3 9PT
(0905) 24872

Post Office Telecommunications
Marketing Department
2-12 Gresham Street
London EC2V 7AG
01-357 2787

Pullen Foundries Ltd
60 Beddington Lane
Croydon
Surrey CR9 4ND
01-684 1416

Queensbury Signs Ltd
19-26 Brunel Road
East Acton
London W3 7UW
01-749 0261

Reading Plastics Ltd
Lysons Avenue
Ash Vale
Farnborough
Hants GU12 5QS
(0252) 23891

Recticel Ltd
18-22 Summerville Road
Bradford
West Yorks BD7 1PY
(0274) 27370/29243

Redland Precast Ltd
PO Box 1
Barrow-upon-Soar
Loughborough
Leics LE12 8LX
(050 96) 2601

Reflecting Roadstuds Ltd
Boothtown
Halifax HX3 6TR
Yorkshire
(0422) 60208/9

**Reinforced Concrete Construction
Co Ltd**
Delph Road
Brierley Hill
Staffs DY5 2RW
(0384) 78079

Rentaplay Ltd
Bentalls
Pipps Hill Industrial Area
Basildon
Essex
(0268) 3391

Road Research Laboratory
Crowthorne
Berks RG11 6AU
(034 46) 3131

Road Research Ltd
28A Great Hales Street
Market Drayton
Shropshire
(0630) 2148/9

Road Signs—Franco Ltd
Boundary Estate
Stafford Road
Fordhouses
Wolverhampton
(0902) 782444

Rotasign Ltd
38 Kenton Road
Kenton
Harrow
Middlesex
01-907 0301

Roto Plastic Containers
King Street
Enderby
Leicester LE9 5NT
(053 729) 4355/6

Ronacrete Ltd
296 Ilford Lane
Ilford
Essex IG1 2SD
01-553 2096

Sanders Tubecrafts Ltd
Burscough Industrial Trading Estate
Higgins Lane
Burscough
Lancs L40 8JB
(0704) 893656

Setright Registers Ltd
Fairfield Road
Bow
London E3
01-980 4102

Sevenoaks Brickworks Ltd
Greatness
Sevenoaks
Kent TN14 5BP
(0732) 59678

Sherbourne Engineering Ltd
Sherbourne Road
Acocks Green
Birmingham B26 1UD
(021 706) 6100

Sloan & Davidson Ltd
Swinnow Lane
Stanningley
Pudsey
West Yorkshire LS28 7XE
(0532) 571892

Smart & Brown Lighting Ltd
Bond Road
Mitcham
Surrey CR4 3YX
01-640 1221

SMP (Landscapes) Ltd
Ferry Lane
Hythe End
Wraysbury
Staines
Middlesex TW19 6HH
(078 481) 2225

South Coast Welders Ltd
Lympne
Hythe
Kent CT21 4LR
(0303) 68112/5

**Southern Metal Fabrications
(Bristol) Ltd**
Parnall Road
Fishponds
Bristol
(0272) 653438

Spooner Qwik-Space
228 Leeds Road
Hull HU8 0DP
(0482) 701801

Sportsmark Ltd
Sportsmark House
Lionel Road
Brentford
Middlesex TW8 9AZ
01-560 2010/2

**Staines Tinware Manufacturing
Co Ltd**
Langley Road
Staines
Middlesex TW18 2EJ
(0784) 59134

Starkey Gardner Ltd
Lady Lane Industrial Estate
Hadleigh
Ipswich IP7 9DG
Suffolk
(047 338) 2525

Stanton and Staveley Ltd
PO Box 72
Nr Nottingham NG10 5AA
(060 72) 322121

Street Furniture Ltd
Horton Road
West Drayton
Middlesex UB7 8JE
(0895) 42607

Sundt Plastics Ltd
New Walk
Hanham
Bristol BS15 3ET
(0272) 672241

Swintex Ltd
Derby Works
Manchester Road
Bury
Greater Manchester BL9 9LX
(061 761) 4933

Tarmac Roadstone Holdings Ltd
50 Waterloo Road
Wolverhampton WV1 4RU
(0902) 22411

Frederick Thomas & Co Ltd
Everton Buildings
Stanhope Street
London NW1
01-387 0111

Thorn Lighting Ltd
Outdoor Lighting Division
Thorn House
Upper St Martin's Lane
London WC2H 9ED
01-836 2444

G Tipper & Co Ltd
Progress House
Castle Lane
Castle Point
Benfleet
Essex
(0702) 554701

Thyssens (GB) Ltd
Burry Box Works
Burry Box Road
Machynys
Llanelli
Dyfed SA15 2DF
(05542) 2244
(0933) 650126

Town and Country Steelcraft Ltd
Reform Road
Maidenhead
Berks SL6 8DA
(0628) 27755

Townscape Products Ltd
176 Loughborough Road
Leicester LE4 5LF
(0533) 65321

Truesigns Ltd
169 Oldbury Road
West Bromwich
West Midlands B70 9DJ
(021) 553 5723

Tully Engineering Co Ltd
Northern Road
Newark
Notts NG24 2ES
(0636) 4496/8

Tyneside Engineering Ltd
Walker Road
Newcastle upon Tyne NE6 1BQ
(0632) 653026/8

UAC International Ltd
UAC Timber Division
PO Box 1
UAC House
Blackfriars Road
London SE1 9UG
01-928 2070

UAC Timber (Wragby)
Wragby
Lincoln LN3 5NE
(067 34) 304

Ubbink-Telmrose Ltd
108 Churchill Road
Bicester
Oxfordshire OX6 7XD
(08692) 41482/3

The Universal Parking Meter Co Ltd
Morley Road
Tonbridge
Kent TN9 1RA
(0732) 358202

Urban Enviroscape Limited
95 Walton Street
London SW3 2HP
01-589 6279

VEB Ltd
Stags End House
Gaddesden Row
Hemel Hempstead
Herts HP2 6HN
(058 285) 3551

Venner
Division of AMF International Ltd
AMF House
Whitby Road
Bristol BS4 4AZ
(0272) 778383

Ward & Co (Letters) Ltd
Maze Street
Barton Hill
Bristol 5
(0272) 553774/553386

Watco (Sales) Ltd
56 Buckingham Gate
London SW1 6AE
01-834 5393

Charles Wicksteed and Co Ltd
Stamford Road Works
Digby Street
Kettering
Northants NN16 8YU
(0536) 517028

Wilson, Walton International (Signs) Ltd
Harrington Road
London SE25 4LX
01-656 4511

D W Windsor Ltd
Stanstead Abbots
Hertfordshire
(0920) 870567

A C Woodrow and Co
Croydon Road
Beckenham
Kent BR3 4BJ
01-650 2283

Geo Wooliscroft & Son Ltd
Hanley
Stoke-on-Trent ST1 3ND
(0782) 284 3832

Wybone Industrial Sales Ltd
Platts Common Industrial Estate
Platts Common
Hoyland
Nr Barnsley
South Yorks
(0226) 744010

Bibliography

British Waterways Board
Waterway Environmental Handbook
1972

Davis, Belfield and Everest
Spon's Architects' and Builders' Handbook
E & F N Spon, published annually

Design Council and the Royal Town Planning Institute
Streets Ahead
1979

Design Council
Street Furniture Catalogue
published biannually

Nicolette Franck
Concrete in the Urban Landscape
Cement and Concrete Association 1973

Greater London Council Department of Architecture and Civic Design
Departmental Standard Drawings

Greater London Council
Modified Greater London Development Plan

Greater London Council
Thamesmead: Infrastructure Design Guide
1975

Derek Lovejoy and Partners
Spon's Landscape Book
E & F N Spon 1980

Ministry of Transport/Scottish Development Department/The Welsh Office
Roads in Urban Areas
HMSO 1967

Ministry of Transport/Scottish Development Department/The Welsh Office
Traffic Signs Manual
HMSO 1977

R Neufert
Architects' Data, The Handbook of Building Types
Halsted Press, New York 1980

Scottish Local Authorities Special Housing Group (SLASH)
External Environment (series of Design Guides) 1973

Cliff Tandy
Handbook of Urban Landscape
The Architectural Press 1972

P Tutt and D Adler
The VNR Metric Handbook of Architectural Standards
Van Nostrand Reinhold, New York 1980

P Tutt and D Adler
The New Metric Handbook
The Architectural Press, London 1979

Geoffrey Warren
Vanishing Street Furniture
David and Charles 1978

The following magazines frequently contain useful articles:

Abitare *Italy*
The Architect *GB*
L'Architettura *Italy*
L'Architecture D'Aujourd'hui *France*
Architectural Association Quarterly *GB*
The Architectural Review *GB*
Ark *Finland*
Arkitektur *Sweden*
Bauen & Wohnen *W Germany*
Bauzeitung *W Germany*
Built Environment *GB*
Bygge Kunst *Norway*
Concrete Quarterly *GB*
Construction *GB*
Design *GB*
Domus *Italy*
Industrial Design *USA*
Landscape Design *GB*
Progressive Architecture *USA*
Sport & Bader & Freizeit-Bauten *W Germany*
Town and Country Planning *GB*
Werk.Archithese *Switzerland*

Index

Credits

Produced in the Department of
Architecture and Civic Design, Greater
London Council.

Architect to the Council
F B Pooley CBE

Technical Policy Architect
Malcolme Gordon

Author
Richard M Cartwright MDes RCA

Contributors
David Ball section 4.1
Roy Burnikell comparative costings
John Earl sections 18.1 and 18.2
Robert Garton comparative costings
Robert Hill section 4.1
Dudley Walters chapter 11

Drawings and photographs
Richard M Cartwright
Graham Freeman
Trevor Gilbert
Leslie Hall
Christopher Stanton
GLC Photographic Unit

Manuscript typing
Ouida Atkins
Kay Handley
Manjeet Mudan
Belinda Mussenden

Graphics and book design
Joe Hale

Editor
David Atwell
Information Officer to the Department of
Architecture and Civic Design, to whom
any enquiries regarding the contents of
this book should be addressed

Richard M Cartwright MDes RCA is an
industrial and environmental designer in
the Design Unit of the GLC Department
of Architecture and Civic Design. He
would like to thank the following for
their general advice:

David Seigle-Morris
Head of the Furniture and Industrial
Design Section of the Design Unit,
Department of Architecture and Civic
Design

L W Hatherly
Assistant Chief Engineer, Maintenance
Division of Construction Branch,
Department of Planning and
Transportation

P C Hoare
Director of Mechanical and Electrical
Engineering

R W Robson-Smith
Chief Planning Architect, Traffic and
Development Branch, Department of
Planning and Transportation